Bay to Ocean

2020

*The Year's Best Writing from the
Eastern Shore Writers Association*

EASTON, MARYLAND

Eastern Shore Writers Association
P.O. Box 1773
Easton, MD 21601
www.easternshorewriters.org

Editorial Board:
Ellen Krawczak
Donna Rothert
Russell Reece

Emily Rich and Tara Elliott, Executive Editors
Emily Rich, Managing Editor
Marie Leonard, Graphic Design

Cover artwork: "Marsh" by Laura Ambler. This image is licensed in perpetuity by the copyright owner, Laura Ambler, to the Eastern Shore Writers Association at no cost for the sole purpose and use as the cover of the Bay to Ocean 2020 anthology and the normal usage in promoting this publication.

CONTENTS

PREFACE 9

IN MEMORIAM 11

Poetry

JANE EDNA MOHLER 13
   To the Publisher

CAROL CASEY 14
   Black and White

AMBER GREEN 15
   I Wasn't Raised This Way

PAT VALDATA 16
   I Post Another Sunset to Facebook

NANCY MITCHELL 30
   Summer Working Tobacco

LAURA SHOVAN 47
   Baking Sourdough

KIM ROBERTS 48
   Fromagerie

CATHERINE CARTER 54
   Boat Woman, St Mary's City

MICHAEL D. JONES 55
   Freedom in the Time of Repression

TARA A. ELLIOTT 71
   Honeysuckle

CAROL CASEY 104
   This Is Not a Dream About Sex

SHARON SHEPPARD 105
   Fidelity

SHARON SHEPPARD 106
   Farewell

SEAN SUN 107
The Last Rose in My Garden

MICHELLE KREINER 108
Beached

NANCY MITCHELL 112
Forensics

CATHERINE CARTER 113
Whippoorwills, Souls

NANCY MCCLOY 115
When the Moon Sleeps

CATHERINE CARTER 116
Things to Love About the Rain

PATRICIA BUDD 118
Bold Coast

NATALIE LOBE 119
The Curative Powers of Salt Water

CATHERINE R. SEELEY 120
The Waterman's Son

TINA RAYE DAYTON 125
What It's Like

TINA RAYE DAYTON 127
The Shell

MEG EDEN. 129
Scrapbooking

MEG EDEN 131
When the Kitchen Sink Leaked

SHARON SHEPPARD 133
Photo: Lake Okoboji, 1956

KRISTIN W. DAVIS 140
Edges

KRISTIN W. DAVIS 141
College Visits

NATALIE LOBE 142
Pack Up the Past

CAROL CASEY 184
Love Letter to the Bohemia River

LAURA SHOVAN 185
Danae Addresses COVID 19

CAROL CASEY 186
Relentless March

CHRISTOPHER T. GEORGE 195
Assateague in the Time of COVID 19

PAT VALDATA 202
Elegy for Toilet Paper

JACK MACKEY 204
Pandemic Blues, Day 43

Fiction

DAVID J. HOFFMAN 21
Seeking Social Justice at Melford HS

COURTNEY FOSTER 36
Cup of Coffee

DONNA ROTHERT 63
Nothing of Insignificance

CHRISTINE BRENNAN 72
Suburban Affairs

KRIS FAATZ 82
Hazel

PAMELA ANDREWS 92
The Mirror

CAROL CASEY 100
Widow

SARAH McGREGOR 143
The Offer

CHRISTOPHER T. GEORGE & ABEL NOBLE 153
Fragment of a Film Script

RICHARD ZAPPA 157
Knowing John Addison

JAMIE BROWN 169
Labyrinth

JOAN COOPER 171
Celia's Audience With the Madman

Nonfiction

KATIE AIKEN RITTER 17
The Asparagus Cutters

CHARLOTTE ZANG 31
The Healing Properties of Tea

JUNE FORTE 49
Weighing In on Weighing In

GEORGE R. MERRILL 50
Waiting

NINA PHILLIPS 56
A Christmas Surprise

MARY PAUER 109
Burn

ELLEN KRAWCZAK 122
Labor Day

DOUG LAMBDIN 134
Sun and Dust

CAROLINE KALFAS 136
Chefs Without a Recipe Box

CHERYL SADOWSKI 187
Only Connect

ELLEN KRAWCZAK 192
Fear Returns

KAREN KENDRA 192
Pandemic Wish List

CAROLINE KALFAS 199
Space to Grow

KAY DREW 206
Pandemic Offering

STEPHANIE LAMOTTE 208
I'd Like to Teach the World to Sing

CONTRIBUTORS 211

PREFACE

Community. It is the thing that binds us in troubled times; the reminder of our connectedness and our shared humanity. The Eastern Shore Writers Association, though geographically dispersed, is a community of individuals drawn together by the need, through words, to make sense of the world.

It is through our words we grapple with one of the most tumultuous years in memory. A frightening virus that leaves us at once terrified and isolated. A re-ignited struggle for racial justice following one of the most widely viewed police killings ever witnessed. A nation seemingly split into bitter encampments.

But it is also through writing that we remark on the wonder of the world outside the twin crises of disease and unrest. We express our awe at the beauty and rhythm of the natural world around us. Share the love and trials of families and relationships. And it is through writing we let loose our creative imaginations, forging fictional realms of intrigue and romance.

Within these pages, ESWA writers take a stand for racial justice and recount acts of kindness that made the world a better place. They chronicle the fear and monotony of COVID-19 and quarantine. They describe the lush sensations of baking sourdough or selecting fine cheese. They lend their words to weighing and waiting, to White Russian exiles, unrepentant hoarders; to lust, betrayal, and regret. To whippoorwills, and rain-softened earth, to salt water, to babies born and to children grown. In short, this small volume encompasses the complexity, messiness, and joy of life.

It has been a great pleasure to read and edit all the wonderful contributions of the members of ESWA. In uncertain times, this community of writers has given me hope.

– Emily Rich, *Co-Executive Editor & Managing Editor*

IN MEMORIAM

This issue is dedicated to the memory of Mala Schipper Schuster Burt (1943-2020). An award winning author, screenwriter, and playwright, Mala's tireless commitment to the Eastern Shore Writers Association and Bay to Ocean conference helped to make both entities what they are today.

Dedication to My Special Friend, Mala Burt

A wife, a mother, a playwright, an author, a confidante, and an extraordinary gardener, especially of those who were her human flowers. She watched us grow, nourished us with wisdom, encouraged us at every turn, and cherished nothing more than a funny story. To all who knew her, she touched our hearts forever. She helped us grow a remarkable, noteworthy and wonderful writer's conference, and I was so very proud to be a part of her sphere of influence to writers on the Eastern Shore and beyond. Rest in peace, my dear, friend. You left us too soon, but your accomplishments will continue to bear fruit for years to come.

– Bonnie Feldstein

Jane Edna Mohler

TO THE PUBLISHER:

Please consider my smeared and saggy
box of fragile, out-of-date jumble.
I've enclosed a roadside mattress, confused
homesickness, my first wedding dress,
and small soil-sweet radishes.

I may regret the dog ears and stains,
my impulse to splash in cold puddles,
spray the reader with gray mud while
I analyze the yearning of box turtles,
and hope those turtles might come to like me.

You'll see that I keep listening for the dead
or the far removed. Wishing I knew if the secret
ingredient they added was fennel or fenugreek.
I pine for their personal obsessions for red chickens
or trash picking. Oddities I miss so deeply.

Thank you for helping me pack all this up.
I'm told that as a group the collection
may be weightier, but not too difficult
to carry. Please seal the box tightly.
I don't want anything to leak.

Carol Casey

BLACK AND WHITE

I am trying to write a poem about a woman,
a black woman, a Black woman who drives a white van
and inside the van are packages from Amazon.
And I'm on my walk and she wants to know if I know
who lives in the house where she has to deliver a package
and not to just anyone but only to the person in there
who is not opening the door.

I wanted this poem to decline from a high conceit
about nature and the country road I walk every day—
yellow wildflowers and goldfinches—and not to take us
to the weedy backyard of the house, where I have gone
to look for a back door, but she does not follow.
She says, "I am afraid."

I hoped this poem, founded in shock and dismay
at her everyday fear, would help salve some pain,
would show us, her and me, a way out of this
old sundown town to where we both can feel safe
and unafraid. The door is closed. The van idles.
I see this poem is not going to get us there.

Amber Green

I WASN'T RAISED THIS WAY

I wasn't raised this way.
I wasn't raised to be this black woman in this America.
I wasn't raised to be this black woman in their America.
I am not prepared for this.
And yet I AM PREPARED FOR THIS

My mother taught me strength and my father instilled pride.
I wasn't raised to watch bodies fall
Blood creating rivers and protest signs have now become our rafts and
tripods our oars ... I was not raised to fight a war
I thought we already won.

I grew up on the taste of victory thanks to sit-ins and yet lived through
the consequences of kneeling.
I was not raised to be this black woman in this America.
I grew up proud of my education and yet today wince at the
compliment of speaking so well.
I was not raised to be this black woman in this America.
My grandfather, cousins, and uncles fought to wave that red white and
blue flag and yet my brother's heart still skips a beat when he no longer
is wearing his military uniform and he sees red white and blue lights.
We were NOT raised to be these BLACK children in this America.

So when black children react like the children of America they were
raised to be ... Think before you question,
Their home training.
Because they were not raised to be children in this America.

Pat Valdata

I POST ANOTHER SUNSET ON FACEBOOK

Well, sure, it was gorgeous, and once upon a time
that seemed reason enough. Because the transience
of those hues. The delicate pink that so soon blooms
blood-orange red, like the Minneapolis skyline,
then crimson, like blood from a face when a knee
cuts off carotid arteries. A knee from a cop's leg.

My grandfather was a white cop in a blue uniform.
I was related to him by blood. Still, he terrified me:
His white hair, his booming voice. That uniform
with polished buttons. The billy club in his belt.
Same breed as this cop, one leg committing murder.
His upper body casual. He didn't give one fuck

about the man he killed, or the cell phone cameras
documenting murder. Those cell phones also take
pictures of toddler granddaughters in party dresses
who grow up to be Karens, of big-game hunters
smug over dead herbivores, of riots, of buildings
on fire, shooting up flames the color of sunsets.

Katie Aiken Ritter

THE ASPARAGUS CUTTERS

They walked the roads on spring nights, men with dark skin and ragged clothing in groups of five or seven or eight, strung across the macadam. I asked questions about them, but got few answers; I was a child in the back seat of an old Buick, and mostly ignored.

They were migrant workers from Puerto Rico who came to pick asparagus. I learned that the term, spoken as a single word '*puertoricans*,' did not refer to their country. It defined them: creatures who followed crops north, who worked in the dirt of farms, who were despised, who were poor.

Sometimes I saw people try spit on them—*spics*, people also called them—from car windows as they passed the men. The spitters would point and laugh, jeering.

Why, I wondered? Even to a little girl, it seemed so very wrong.

The men walked the roads because that was all they could do after work. They had no cars. There was nothing for miles around. If they were fortunate enough to pile into the back of a pickup truck to ride to a country town, white people moved away from them as if the *puertoriccans* were infected with something, and watched, eyes narrowed, squinting.

I still loathe that look: the squint of racism. *You aren't equal. Your kind isn't welcome here.*

The Puerto Ricans toiled in fields outside my town. They bent, cut, and stepped forward; bent, cut, and stepped, harvesting tender spears of asparagus. I once asked where they lived, and my mother pointed to a shed: low-slung, brutally plain concrete block with tiny windows through which no breeze would ever freshen the air.

Barely any toilet facilities, my mother muttered.

"How do they take baths?" I asked.

"I don't know," she whispered, and turned away.

I frowned. Who could live like that?

They sent the money they earned home to their families. *To children like me, I wondered? To mothers like my mother?*

I know how most people thought of them: as dogs. Not the coddled well-fed household-member dogs of today, but the chained-out-back, supper-scraps dogs of a 1950's farm, dogs I had seen cursed and kicked. Nobody cared about the Puerto Ricans. They were insignificant beasts of labor.

In the still-segregated Eastern Shore of those days, I also grew up hearing the word '*nigger*' regularly. Nobody thought much about that. Nobody white, that is. There was no respect; there was no *intention* of respect. Dark-skinned people, '*niggers*' and '*spics*,' were not like 'us.' They had nothing in common with 'us'. *We did not need to care about them.*

I say this bluntly because there are people who do not remember that kind of meanness. Lots of people *do* remember; they are often people of color. But even as a child, I knew it was wrong. I am sure that other people knew it was wrong, too.

I used to send silent greetings to the workers on the county roads: *hello. We don't all hate you.* I would breathe out hope. It was all I knew to do.

But it was unchangeable, I believed. It was the way it was and always would be. People I loved cast proud votes for George Wallace as president, trusting his hatred for people of color would save 'us' from the ghastly prospect of having to acknowledge black people as equals.

In college, I heard of a man named Cesar Chavez. Something about grapes and migrant workers. (Much later—because women, too, did not matter as much then—I heard of Dolores Huerta.)

Chavez sounded brave. Thinking of the asparagus cutters, I raised my fist in solidarity—but inwardly thought, such a shame. *So much hope and effort, but nothing will change.* What did one man, one woman, a bunch of liberal students matter? The problem was too big. Unchangeable.

I was right...and I was wrong.

I was right in what I instinctively understood as a child, that the racism all around me was a terrible thing. But I was wrong to believe that efforts of people who envisioned change were doomed.

That was years ago. This year brought George Floyd.

The uprisings and protests after his death contrasted with my sad cynicism of earlier days to show me how wrong I had been. Something *did* change: across the farthest reaches of the world, people stood up for a man they'd never known. One by one by one, they stood up.

One human mattered, regardless of how seemingly insignificant.

"George Floyd knee on neck." Type those words on a keyboard, and watch the last seven minutes and forty-three seconds of a man's life. Listen to people beg Derek Chauvin to get off Floyd. Watch Chauvin, hands in his pockets, uniform tight across his muscled chest, smirk as he looks down at George, adjusts his knee, presses harder; whistling almost, as he casually killed the man—a man for whom Chavin had no respect, no *intention* of respect; a human being Chauvin decided just didn't matter because George was troubled, and poor, and had a different color skin.

The images I watched are burned into my mind. They are burned into our national conscience.

We still have a long, *long* way to go, but I'm grateful to see 'people like us'—white people—not just whispering the *hello* of a powerless child, but standing with people of color to demand what our Pledge of Allegiance promises: *justice for all.*

We owe it, because we have done them wrong for so long. I heard, astonished, as Josh and Chuck of the podcast *STUFF YOU SHOULD KNOW* spoke of J. Edgar Hoover's political campaign against Black Panthers, whose primary 'bad' action was to feed and educate impoverished children of color in American cities. Hoover, in a position of public trust, had done wrong—and we believed him. I heard those two white-as-white-can-be podcasters describe their love for 'Soul Train' and what it meant to black communities. Nobody I knew growing up would have admitted to liking it. But I heard Chuck say he had, and I whispered across the airwaves, *me too.*

The bubble of misinformation and mistrust is big and it is tough.

But it is not impervious. It can be broken.

George Floyd's death brought a growing awareness that 'unchangeable' is a big lie. It brought burning desire to stop four hundred years of seeing people as insignificant simply because they have no wealth, or if they are of color.

George has helped us to stop our squinting. His murder helped us to just see. See humans. See people. Not 'blacks,' not *'puertoriccans,'* not 'whites'...not your-kind-versus-our-kind. Just 'us.'

We each must choose: follow the legacy of those who spit on migrant workers simply because of the circumstances of birth? Narrow our eyes and squint at all who are different from us, creating a *'them'* we can push down and climb over? Tell ourselves that today's *'they'* have nothing to do with today's *'us'?*

Or will we have the innocent wisdom of a child, realizing something is wrong and doing our bit, however small, day by day, to right it? Will we offer our hand in help to people like Congressman John Lewis and Wall-of-Vets protestors?

I never thought I'd wear a mask like people on Asian television—yet because of COVID, I now cannot imagine leaving my car without one. We never imagined homeschooling for every American child, yet here we are. Unchangeable things change.

Emboldened by once-unthinkable changes from the pandemic, will we find courage to confront and change wrongs we may never have realized? Will our actions of defiance start as a whisper, but become stronger as we take one step after another, become more determined as we choose to work towards that which must change?

I love the backroads of Cecil and Kent County where I grew up. I love the broad fields of the Eastern Shore, the tall oaks, the quiet tidewater. I love them *so much.*

And I love the land and the strong, beautiful ideals of the United States of America. I love its promise of goodness, and fairness to all.

We have good work to do. But it can be scary work: friends of mine still have the 'squint'. I feel nervous confronting them. Neighbors I care about repeat lies from hate-mongering news outlets, and appalled, I struggle to be brave, to find the right response.

Saying this, gently, works: "I see it differently."

We don't have to get it perfect. We just have to be brave enough to try.

Our Pledge of Allegiance lights the way: when we see people not experiencing "justice for all", we can't just mouth the Pledge. We must be brave enough to make those shining words true, for all of us.

As we hack an imperfect path through the wrongs of the past towards a better future, may we encourage one another, because your attempts matter. Mine matter. Every human matters, and every striving for goodness matters.

Faltering, fearful, perhaps messy though our attempts may be, we become stronger just for trying. Our combined actions, perfect or not, create a community: first a trickle, eventually a tsunami of human desire to change the once-unchangeable, to sweep away racism.

We can do it, my friends. We can do it. Onward.

Written by Katie Aiken Ritter on July 31, 2020 in honor of the courageous young man who faced the 'unchangeable' and became Congressman John Robert Lewis.

David Hoffman

SEEKING SOCIAL JUSTICE AT MELFORD HIGH SCHOOL

The year 1968 was one of the most tumultuous in U.S. history, with the shocking assassinations of Rev. Martin Luther King, Jr., and Robert F. Kennedy within two months of one another. The young of the nation were screaming for social justice, including racial equality, gender equality, and opposition to the escalating Vietnam war. Songs of expression were the norm including James Brown's "Say it Loud, I'm Black and Proud," the Beatles' "Revolution," and the Rascals' "People Got to be Free."

It was early fall in Melford, a city in the greater Boston area. The leaves hadn't begun to change color yet and the days were still warm, but the nights were beginning to cool down. Benny Shapiro's family had just relocated from Rhode Island so his father could pursue a Ph.D. in sociology at Harvard, after struggling for almost five years to make a career of writing.

The Shapiros had moved from the grandparents' spacious waterfront home to a hundred-dollar-a-month frame house on a side street in a mainly blue-collar neighborhood. This section of town was known as the Lowlands, but some called it Little Italy. However, not all the residents were of Italian heritage. There were four or five black families, including the next door neighbors, all of whom were deep-rooted in the neighborhood. There were also Jewish, Greek, and Armenian families, all part of this close-knit neighborhood. In contrast, the elite east side of town was inhabited by wealthy white professionals and businessmen. Ornate Victorian homes and opulent brick and stone houses with mature shade trees and manicured hedges were abundant on the east side.

It was a cool evening and Benny and his dad and their new neighbors from both sides had been sitting around a picnic table over a bottle of wine in the Shapiros' back yard. Dr. Thompson, a Harvard-educated high school and community college history teacher, laid his pipe down for the moment. Then, in his well-punctuated Harvard diction, he slowly and deliberately began to talk about his family history. "My grandfather was a slave on a large Virginia tobacco plantation. For a slave, he was more fortunate than some. He worked as a house slave and carpenter for the plantation rather than in the fields. The owner's wife had a maiden sister who lived with them and was a school teacher. When grandpa was a small boy, she took it upon herself to teach him to read and write. When he attained his freedom, he made his way north to Boston where he had family and was offered work as a railroad Pullman porter. Later, he and his son, my father, who had acquired a high school education, started a small catering business in Boston's Roxbury section. The business did well enough to help me through Northeastern University where I graduated with honors in U.S. history. Then, I was able to secure a fellowship towards a Ph.D. at Harvard. But it was hard finding employment even with the degree. Eventually, a position for a high school history teacher opened and I was hired here at Melford over ten years ago. Now I also teach two evenings a week at a community college."

Benny's dad set his glass of wine aside. "My ancestors may also have been slaves in ancient Egypt and suffered persecution in modern times. I lost my grandparents in the Jewish Holocaust in Nazi-occupied Poland. I'm a Sephardic Jew with roots going back to the Spanish Inquisition when Jews were either forced to convert or were driven out. My ancestors chose to resettle in Tunisia. Later they emigrated to Poland, then, before the Holocaust, my parents emigrated to the U.S. A lot of people look at Benny and me and think we are Sicilian, given our olive skin and wavy black hair. But that's OK with me.

Mr. Nazarian smiled. "Well, I guess that makes us all minority victims of oppression. My grandparents were also persecuted in the Armenian Genocide perpetrated by the Ottoman Empire Turks. I too lost grandparents and many of their family friends. Fortunately, my parents escaped and emigrated to an Armenian community nearby in Watertown. Although we're Armenians, we are also Middle Easterners and are sometimes viewed as Arabs around here. Hell, just look at the three of us here. Even if we had the cash, there's not a damn realtor around here who'd dare show us a house on the swanky east side of town. We'd all have to white-powder our faces first. Now if we were extra lucky, maybe we'd get a house on one of the hillside streets here on the westside. Italian families have made it there."

Benny's dad added, "Well, Jews own nice homes in parts of Rhode Island where we came from and here in Newton and Brookline, so I don't understand."

Mr. Nazarian continued, "The same holds for Armenians in Watertown and Belmont."

Then Dr. Thompson added, "There sure are a lot of us black folk in Roxbury and Dorchester, with a few of us in other communities, but we just never seem to be located in the choice sections of town."

The following morning, Benny and Dr. Thompson's son Tommy both piled into the back of Dr. Thompson's five-year-old Plymouth Fury for the short ride to Melford High. The car slowed to a crawl as it passed by the wide overhanging arches in front of Melford High School. Both teens hopped out and once in the building waited in front of the locked homeroom door. Both were in the eleventh grade. Tommy, known as "Rabbit" for his speed on the track, was also captain of the cross country team and had convinced Benny to join. They were early but Tommy's dad was their homeroom teacher and history teacher. He was the only black teacher in the high school with more than 50 teachers.

In a few minutes, Dr. Thompson was with them again to open the homeroom door. It was always quite a surprise to enter his homeroom because the shelves along the walls and the wide indoor windowsills were adorned with beautiful handcrafted pottery, including brightly colored vases, beautifully sculpted figurines, and pots containing plants. The room had all the appearance of a fine arts teacher's office, but it was the history teacher's office, featuring Dr. Thompson's handcrafted art. The display was periodically rotated with new works of art. On his desk sat a most beautiful sculpted figurine of a black angel and a white angel sitting side by side on a stone bench with an inscription, "God loves us all."

After a full day of classes, Benny skipped cross country practice since he'd sprained his ankle the day before on the rough terrain. As he sat waiting for Tommy in the back of Dr. Thompson's homeroom office, in marched Martha, the principal's daughter. Her sandy blonde hair was piled and cut to resemble the signature style of Jackie Kennedy, as was her attire. Her green cat eyes never acknowledged Benny's presence, even though they'd been in classes together since the start of the year.

She approached Dr. Thompson and said coldly, "You made an error grading my history quiz."

Dr. Thompson, attired in his usual gray suit and tie, politely offered her a seat. "I try to grade all quizzes very carefully, always giving them two go-overs." He patiently proceeded to check off all the marking points of the individual questions in front of her and then totaled them, coming out with the same score originally issued.

Martha countered, "You under-graded me on the four short essay questions."

Dr. Thompson shifted his tortoise-framed glasses and scratched the bald spot on his head with a look of puzzlement. Then he went through each of the four questions with what the key points for a correct answer should have included. "I gave you the benefit of the doubt on all of these. You really had only half of what was required, but I gave you 30 out of 40 points."

Martha pleaded, "Can't you please upgrade me. I'm an A student and I only received a B."

"I'm sorry Martha, I have to grade fairly for all. You did better than quite a few in the class and there'll be at least six more quizzes, giving you an opportunity to improve."

"But Dr. Thompson, after all, I **am** the principal's daughter and I **am** an A student!"

"Sorry, Martha, better luck next time."

Now angered, Martha smirked and belted out, "If my father had been principal at the time you were interviewed, he never would have hired you except maybe as part of the janitorial staff." With that, she slammed her clipboard on his desk and marched out, glaring at Benny as she passed by.

Benny quietly took it all in, thinking that Martha had just confirmed what he'd been hearing all along and had observed during encounters in the hallway: She was one self-serving entitled "little princess" as his other neighborhood friend, Peter Nazarian, had dubbed her.

A few minutes later Tommy came in still sweaty from his run, "And where were you today, Turtle?"

"Tommy, my twisted ankle from yesterday didn't feel like competing with a Rabbit today. Tomorrow I'll give it a go with you."

With that they piled into his dad's car for the ride home. Dr. Thompson, not his chipper self, remained silent during the ride.

Once home, Benny took Tommy aside in his backyard and quietly recounted what had occurred with Martha in his father's homeroom. Tommy was both saddened and angered, but not surprised. He said it was best not to say anything to his dad about it. It would only be more hurtful for him. Benny didn't hesitate to inform his own parents. His parents were furious, being Jews who'd experienced social injustice growing up in the form of schoolyard bullying and rampant discrimination. They'd become part of a highly active local Unitarian organization for social justice. Mr. Shapiro remembered the days at public recreational sites in northwest Baltimore when signs were posted, "NO JEWS or DOGS ALLOWED."

Martha had a small close-knit clique of confidants who shared her views. Benny and Peter Nazarian often overheard them talking in corners of the hallway with catty comments about other students and sometimes teachers whom they considered to be socially unacceptable according to their own prejudiced standards and bloated egos. Peter's sister, Mariam, heard more through the female grapevine. She knew they referred to her brother as Ali Baba, saying he should be riding on a carpet instead of a car. They referred to Benny as little Shylock, accusing his father of being a loan shark. And now given what had just occurred, Martha was on the warpath against Dr. Thompson and his son. She came just short of using the N-word on him, stating, "We don't need a black rabbit as captain of our cross country team, a disgrace to the school."

For the second half of the school year, there were plans to offer a half-year course in Introductory Civics, a topic that the present troubled times were begging for. The school board had approved and put it on the schedule. No new hire would be required since Dr. Thompson had a Ph.D. from Harvard in US history and government. Dr. Thompson was eagerly looking forward and had already selected a textbook. However, there was a fly in the ointment as far as Mr. Appleton, the principal, was concerned. His daughter had signed up for a short course in speech and drama that had been offered in the same time slot now designated for civics. The drama course would still be offered, but as the last class of the day. His daughter had become accustomed to using the last hour of the day as a study hall period when she'd been permitted to leave early for any purpose, including cheerleading practice. The moment she was informed of the change in schedule, she became irate and adamant about not permitting the change.

Her father, Mr. Jonathon Henry Appleton III, was proud of his Boston Brahmin heritage and belonged to several clubs exclusive to Boston blue bloods just like him. These clubs tended to subtly promote racial and ethnic prejudice, reaffirming his own convictions. He'd grown up in a wealthy banking family and attended choice prep schools, followed by a degree from Dartmouth. He resented the fact that "Mister Thompson," as he addressed him rather than "Dr.," was a black man who'd been accepted into a Harvard Ph.D. program that had rejected him. He was totally supportive of his daughter's wishes. He contacted the school board and the superintendent of schools, claiming that he thought the civics course should be put on hold for another year since Mr. Thompson already had a heavy teaching load and needed more time to adequately prepare for the new course.

When Dr. Thompson was contacted, he was quick to inform the school board that he'd already taught a community college-level course in civics and his present schedule was no obstacle. So, the civics course would remain as scheduled. Upon hearing this, Martha had a tantrum, but there was little more her father could do to appease her. In her rage, she was quick to pin the blame on "Mister Thompson" who, of course, had no say as to when the course would be scheduled.

A few days later Benny and Tommy stood waiting for his dad to park the car and open the homeroom door. As soon as Tommy pushed the door open, it was immediately apparent that something was not right. All around the room the many fine handcrafted planting pots, vases, and even the figurines that his dad had so artfully crafted were lying in pieces on the hard floor. They appeared to have been hurled to the floor with some force, given how shattered the pottery was. Particles on the floor ranging from earth color to bright turquoise, deep blue, and pea-green were intermingled with torn coleus and geranium plants. Dr. Thompson's prized figurine of the two angels was nowhere to be seen. On only one other occasion in his ten years had a vase of flowers been found broken, when it had been seated too close to a busy corner.

Benny observed Dr. Thompson's demeanor quickly change from shock to sadness. All of his struggle for acceptance in a largely white-dominated academic world and school system had been rolled backward. He wiped his eyes with a pocket handkerchief. Tommy gently began stroking his poor dad on the back. Benny's eyes were glued to the floor in disbelief. What could so kind a man have done to deserve such treatment?

Dr. Thompson walked several doors down to the principal's office to report the apparent vandalism while Benny and Tommy stood waiting with a large dustpan to assist with the cleanup before the students would arrive in the next half hour. Principal Appleton soon came in to observe and contacted the chief of police stationed nearby who arrived within minutes to take a few pictures and inspect for fingerprints. Since the door had been locked, it was concluded that it was most likely someone affiliated with the school who had access to a key. The principal looked disturbed, but oddly, seemed to be concealing a smirk. As soon as the chief departed, Benny, Tommy, and his father cleaned up the debris.

Martha arrived at homeroom early, contrary to her customary tardiness. She'd never greeted or even acknowledged Benny or Tommy before but today looked directly at them with her green cat eyes and inquired with an exaggerated expression of surprise, "Is there something different here today?"

They merely shrugged, as though they had no more idea than she did. Dr. Thompson managed to compose himself, and dryly read a few homeroom announcements for the day. Some of the students appeared to notice the missing pottery and plants but most likely assumed that he had chosen to rotate the display as he periodically had done before.

Benny and Tommy were unaware of Martha's fury over the drama and civics course conflict until Peter informed them that his sister Mariam had witnessed Martha ranting about it to her inner circle and casting the blame upon Dr. Thompson.

Benny looked at Tommy, "If that little princess really believes your dad is solely responsible, do you really think she is wicked enough to have destroyed his art?"

Tommy wrung his hands, holding his head down, solemnly nodding in agreement.

They had to come up with a plan. Benny, Tommy, and Peter sat huddled around the Shapiros' picnic table after school sipping Cokes, but remained undecided.

The following day in the school cafeteria at noon, Mariam took all three aside to offer a bombshell. "Martha boasted to her little groupie circle that she did it. She also pocketed the angel figurine, dusted the black angel with white powder, and taped over the inscription, restating it to read "God loves us all white" rather than the original "God loves us all." Then she passed it around her circle of groupies. However, one of her groupies felt enough was enough and defected, telling me all."

Tommy was hesitant about telling his dad immediately. But Benny and Peter decided to confide in their fathers, who were more than irate, pounding the table and shouting, "That privileged little princess deserves to be horsewhipped and put in juvenile detention." Before taking any action, they needed to discuss it with Tommy's dad. All the dads met in the Shapiros' house. Tommy's dad had been somewhat stunned upon hearing the evidence, but not totally surprised. If anything, it was some relief to know that the perpetrator had been a single individual, not a group. It was the action of a spoiled entitled teen with an asinine unfounded motive. He said it would be his preference to talk to the principal privately with the allegations.

The following afternoon he made an appointment with the principal and as calmly as he could proceeded, "Jonathan, I've known you for five years as our principal. I've been told by several students that your daughter, Martha, has been very angry with me over the scheduling of the civics course which I had absolutely no say in. She thinks it's all my fault, and in her anger, vandalized my office, destroying my art and still has possession of my most treasured figurine of two angels."

The principal stiffened and looked directly at him with a rather unconvincing expression of surprise. "I'll have to talk to her. I know she's strong-willed, but I really don't think she's capable of such a thing."

The following morning, they met again and the principal proceeded, "I spoke with Martha last night and she denies having done anything, saying she'd seen some players from a rival football team hanging around the building over the weekend. But she said she's sorry to hear what happened. I don't think our school insurance will cover your personal art, but what I'd like to do is write you a check for three hundred dollars to help compensate for the loss."

Mr. Thompson blinked and replied, "I spent hundreds of hours creating my sculptures. No amount of money can bring them back. I don't need your check, but I wish I had my missing angel figurine back."

The principal gravely nodded in agreement.

The following morning, he summoned Dr. Thompson again into his office saying, "A member of the janitorial staff found your figurine undamaged early this morning on a hallway shelf near the entrance. Evidently the thieves decided not to keep it."

Dr. Thompson smiled weakly as he accepted his prized figurine and then quietly walked out of the office.

Benny's dad and Peter's dad pleaded with Dr. Thompson to hire a civil rights attorney. In fact, there were several they knew who'd most likely take the case pro bono. His answer was no, he wasn't interested in pursuing it. He'd already experienced his share of stress and challenges in his early years interacting with a sometimes-hostile white community. He enjoyed teaching history and his leisure time sculpting and attending Tommy's track and cross country meets.

However, the jury of public opinion is often a far more powerful force than the legal system. The word had spread and many of Martha's inner circle had defected, leaving her isolated and shunned. Many teachers had lost all respect for the principal, feeling he had been far from candid and should have held his daughter accountable. The word traveled to the superintendent of schools, who had been with the system for nearly twenty years and readily listened to his veteran teachers who'd been around equally long. He considered it was time for a change, assigned the principal a temporary position in his own office, and placed the assistant principal, well-liked by students and teachers alike, in an acting capacity.

Martha and her father decided that she would complete her senior year at a girls' prep school in Boston. He had received an offer at the same school for the position of assistant dean.

As for Dr. Thompson, he continued doing what he enjoyed doing best, teaching, sculpting, and attending his son's track and cross country meets. Before long, Dr. Thompson sculpted a white female devil figurine, which he soon cast aside for fear of it bringing bad luck.

Nancy Mitchell

SUMMER WORKING TOBACCO

Sun down, and we'd all be sweat-stunk from primin' leaf by leaf
since sun up, sticky with amber ooze tacky as Gorilla Glue, but
nothing a quick dip in the bile-green runoff creek behind the pulp
mill couldn't eat right off our skin, be it red, yellow, black or white
"all precious in Jesus' sight" as the Bible-School-Teacher-Boss-Lady
liked to say. Bullshit--or what else but bullshit does she have some
come up to the Big-House for lunch, wash up first in her pretty
bathroom with a bar of sweet-smelling shell-shaped soap, then dry
hands on fluffy pink towels before sitting down to the table to eat
fried drumsticks and breasts, cornbread, and lima beans on her
flowered plates—after she says grace, of course—while some pick at
wings, backs, and necks from the brown Piggly Wiggly bag set out
on the porch with a roll of paper towels to pass between?

Well, maybe our skin'd come clean in the creek, but our tees and
dungarees—lordy—that's another story. Grit, 'bacco leaf-debris
gum-stuck and all our Mamas be damned if they'd let us gunk up
their washing machines. So, we'd throw 'em over the chain link
fence, power hose off what shit we could and pray they'd be dry by
the time that Carolina sun showed up like a big orange fuzzed with
phosphorus fog. Five times outta ten, you could bet a split six-pack
of Pabst or half a pouch of Red Man chaw those fukin' jeans still'd
be damp, stank and stiff, and we like to never pull 'em on.

Charlotte Zang

THE HEALING PROPERTIES OF TEA

I was almost afraid to open the box, never having received a gift so precious. The outside said in big, bold letters, "Porcelain Toy Tea Set." I ignored the word "toy" and focused on the word "porcelain." Surely porcelain, whatever that was, made it very special.

I had seen a show on television about people who lived in Japan and the special tea ceremonies they had. The costumes and dishes and flowers were so beautiful and the people were smiling. Oh, how I wished I could go there! I was fascinated by something that was so very different from everything in my little world, which extended only as far as the front yard.

My family had no visitors or neighbors and I had never been anywhere. There were no vacations, but I knew from television that those were only for rich people. My summers were spent mostly in the big garden behind our house and in the kitchen. Long rows of corn, tomatoes, peppers, green beans, peas, lima beans, potatoes, squash, cucumbers, onions, and carrots were spread out in front of me every day, just waiting to be weeded or picked while mosquitoes and sheep flies buzzed overhead and bit my arms before I could slap them away. When I started in the morning, my bare feet made little tracks in the dark, damp soil that was soft and cool. I liked that better than walking on the dusty cracked ground when the sun was blazing hot after lunch.

I was afraid of a lot of things, but my biggest fear was being stung by a tomato worm. They were the same color as the tomato plant so they were very hard to spot. I knew for sure that they were poisonous (my brother said that I could die if I got stung), so I was very careful when picking tomatoes. But that meant I went slower and didn't always finish the row.

I didn't like picking corn because the leaves could cut like a knife and some of the ears were full of smut, nasty-looking stuff all swollen and gray, puffing out of the top of the ear. It was an ugly surprise when I pulled it down to drop it in the bushel basket that I drug along beside me.

I could pick peas and beans without too much trouble, although once I wasn't paying attention and pulled up a whole bean plant. I looked around to make sure nobody saw me and quickly put the drooping plant back in the ground, packing dirt around the broken roots and kept going, pretending it never happened. Maybe one of my brothers would get blamed for it.

When picking was done for the day, there were hours spent husking corn on the back steps and snapping beans or shelling peas and limas spread out on newspaper on the same table where we ate dinner. We canned beans and froze sweet corn at night because my mother couldn't bear the heat that came from boiling and canning until after the sun went down. She didn't seem to mind the night bugs–the gnats and little black insects with hard shells that flipped themselves around instead of crawling–that gathered around the ceiling light. They worried me something awful. The longer we worked, the bigger the swarm got. The kitchen must have been too hot for some of them because in the morning I swept up a whole bunch that lay dead even though they were hard to see, mixed in with the squiggly pattern on the floor. I don't know where the other bugs went in the daytime but I hoped they went back outside.

My first trip away from home was on a school bus to attend first grade where the only person I knew was my brother. He told me two things: I wasn't allowed to cry and I wasn't allowed to talk to him. That didn't help me at all. At least schoolwork was pretty easy--just do what I was told. Line up. Be quiet. Read a story and write what it was about. That was a whole lot easier than picking tomatoes. I leaned my head against the bus window on the ride home and thought about the people in Japan. It gave me hope that a different kind of life was possible even if it wasn't very likely.

I remembered those happy people in Japan when I added the tea set to my Christmas list that year. I never dreamed that I might actually get it. But sitting there on the floor in front of the tree on Christmas morning was the Classic Blue Bird design box set, just what I had circled in the Sears Christmas catalog, the *Wish Book*. My mother only shopped at Sears. Never anywhere else, except the A&P store on Thursday mornings and Stanley's newsstand where she bought my father's newspapers every Sunday. She placed her Sears order over the phone and picked it up at the catalog store in town. If there was anywhere else to buy things, I sure didn't know about it. I thought everything came from Sears.

That Christmas, just like every year, there were no names on the gifts. My brothers and sisters and I rushed down the steps from our three bedrooms and made our way into the living room. There were seven unwrapped gifts around the tree that we had put up and decorated the day before. One gift for each of us.

As I hurried to get to the tree, I nearly tripped on the hem of the heavy flannel gown I wore. The traditional Christmas Eve gift from my grandmother, it felt like cardboard and was a size too large, but I had been required to wear it. At least it was better than the too-small slippers she gave me last year. That's all she ever gave us, nightgowns and pajamas or slippers.

My older brothers and sisters quickly selected their gifts, though I can't be sure what they were, and my younger sister was playing with some sort of baby toy, so the tea set must be mine.

I couldn't take my eyes off the box. The picture showed white dishes with a dainty blue pattern. A tree with two birds sitting on the branches was surrounded by a scrolling blue border in a swirling design. I had never seen birds like that but decided that they must be the kind of birds that live in Japan. White birds with blue feathers, a big head, and short, pointy blue beaks.

The words on the box said, "An Oriental-inspired formal tea set she'll use proudly." Formal. See, it was important. I knew it! I looked closely and saw very small letters that read, "Yamada Toshio Shoten–Made in Japan." It was official! Just like the picture in the *Wish Book:* service for six with teapot, creamer, and sugar bowl. I quickly scrawled my name on the box, labeling it as mine, claiming ownership in my best six-year-old penmanship, just like I learned in school.

An orange Nerf ball sailed by, followed by my brother lurching in front of me to retrieve it. Instinctively I moved to guard my new possession.

"Hey! What do you have there? Is it for your doll baby?" he taunted. "Let me see!"

I silently held my ground, defiant even though I knew he had ultimate power. Soon he became bored with bothering a little sister and resumed playing with the rest of the boys, throwing the Nerf ball at the new basketball hoop fastened over the door of the hall closet.

My attention turned back to my special present. Gingerly I removed the box top, anxious to see if the set was as I had imagined. Inside, the contents rested in their own special pink partitioned sections. Plates with cardboard dividers, a stack on each side. One type of plate was a saucer to go under the teacup and the bigger one was for sugar cookies (at least that's what I decided). The creamer and sugar bowl were located in little pink square spaces between the plates. Above them were the cups, each nestled safely within their own little divider. The teapot occupied the prominent center section with the lid to it and the sugar bowl to the right of it.

All of this was new to me. At our house, we only served iced tea, usually in tall glasses or plastic cups, and we certainly didn't have a teapot of any sort. Our dishes didn't have any birds or swirls on them. They were plain and chipped and they didn't match. None of them was as nice-looking as these. That's the way it was: Everything we owned was plain. Nothing pretty and definitely nothing fancy. We had things that we needed and apparently we didn't need pretty things.

I had no idea why the set included something called a creamer, but if it was in there, it must be necessary. I asked a girl at school about it and she said that her mother used a creamer when she put milk in hot tea. I'd never seen anyone drink hot tea and didn't even know that tea could be served hot. Putting milk in it seemed strange, but if that's what they did in Japanese tea ceremonies, then it must be right.

I was so careful with this valuable tea set that I never opened the box when anyone else was around. I didn't want my brothers to use the plates as miniature Frisbees or break the handle off the teapot. They could be so clumsy! No, this was special, and it was mine, and I was determined to protect it.

On days when I believed it was safe, I filled the teapot with iced tea (without the ice), and if I had any cookies, I put them on the plate beside my cup. I poured a tiny amount of tea in the little cup, placed it on the saucer, and then slowly sipped in the most formal way I could imagine, just like the people I had seen on television. And when I was done dreaming of being born into a different family during another time in a faraway place, I carried the dishes to the sink and washed each one carefully. Instead of leaving them in the drainer to dry where they were in danger of being broken, I dried them individually and put them away in their secret compartments. Then I tucked the box in the back of my closet under a blanket, hidden from anyone who might be rummaging for the Magic Eight Ball or the Parcheesi game.

Today when I notice the tea set in its box on the shelf, I am amazed that it has survived at all, and even more incredulous that every single piece is still there, intact, with each item right where it belongs. The pattern is worn and faded in some spots (just like me), having rubbed against the corrugated liner during many moves to new locations, but overall, it is just as I remember it. The birds are still perched in their same positions, frozen in time as symbols of hope and possibility.

Courtney Foster

CUP OF COFFEE

Olivia hummed a little ditty as she dropped a fresh coffee filter into the top of the coffeemaker. Hovering her nose over the open silver package, she closed her eyes and took a whiff.

The customer sitting at the counter cleared his throat and she glanced over at him. "Sorry." She smiled. "I just love the smell of fresh coffee grounds in the morning."

He looked at his watch. "I suppose it is after midnight."

"Are you ready to order?" she asked with a broad smile and her hands on her hips.

"Been ready," he huffed. "I'll take a number 7." He looked up from his menu at the pencil sticking out of her curly, jet-black updo. "You're not gonna write it down?"

Liv looked around the virtually empty diner. The only patrons were a couple of lovebirds, a young man in a booth on the opposite side of the restaurant, and the old fart sitting in front of her at the counter.

"I think I got it. NUMBER 7!" she shouted over her shoulder.

In no time, Liv's customer was getting busy with a stack of fluffy pancakes and she got to work refilling the salt and pepper shakers. Then the door across from the bathrooms creaked open. The manager emerged from his office, yawning and scooping gunk from the corners of his eyes that had accumulated during his nightly nap.

"Liv," he barked. "Why is he still here?"

"Who's that now?" she asked, feigning deep concentration on securing a top to a salt shaker. Then, against her better judgment, she looked up at him. It was a quick glance, but long enough to read the irritation written between the lines in his forehead.

"Come on, Liv, I'm not in the mood for games. You know exactly who I'm talkin' about." He nodded in the young man's direction. "The vagrant over in the booth."

"He's not a vagrant, Tom. He's a university student. You can clearly see the school I.D. hanging from his backpack."

"Well, he's been comin' in here for two weeks and hardly ever orders anything. I'm gettin' him outta here," he said as he took two substantial steps toward his rightful place in hell.

Liv grabbed his arm. "No," she hissed. "It's finals time, and he's not bothering anybody."

Tom stared at the fingers wrapped around his forearm until she remembered how much she needed that job and released her grip. "The club down the street is about to let out and he's takin' up a whole booth. If he ain't payin'; he ain't stayin'."

A list of the other places still open at that time of night ran through her mind. There were other diners within walking distance, two others to be exact. They were popular truck stops frequented by folks looking for more than a cup of coffee and a short stack. She shuddered at the thought of that young man being cast out and stumbling upon one of those places.

Tom raised his brow. "Well?"

"Ok. Ok. I'll take care of it."

Liv could almost feel Tom's glare burning a hole in her back as she approached the young man.

"What can I getcha?" she asked cheerfully with her hands on her hips.

"Nothin', ma'am. I'm fine," he said without looking up from his laptop. And she didn't expect him to. In all the weeks he had been coming to the diner, the only time he looked away from his computer screen was to jot down a note or two.

"Ok, sounds good," she said, nodding vigorously. She turned around and made her way back over to the counter and her fuming boss.

"What the hell are you doing?" Tom asked as Liv poured a cup of coffee and plated a slice of pie.

She shrugged. "You said if he ordered something he could stay."

"Wow. A whopping $3.50 for five hours of booth space. Your bleeding heart's gonna ruin us both, Liv," he warned as she retraced her steps across the diner.

"Here you go!" she said, placing the coffee and pie on the table a safe distance from the laptop.

The young man looked up at her. Until that moment, she had only seen his profile hunched over the computer. A tiny gasp escaped from her throat as feelings of distress and delight competed for dominance. Bags and dark circles that usually made a person look old and worn out surrounded the most beautiful and brightest amber eyes she had ever seen. He couldn't have been more than fifteen. This wasn't a man stealing booth space, he was a boy, and a stressed-out one at that.

"I think you made a mistake, ma'am." His eyes darted around the empty restaurant. "I didn't order anything."

"Oh, I know. I thought you might need a pick-me-up. You've been here for hours and haven't eaten a thing."

The boy hung his head. "I'm sorry. You guys probably don't much like folks comin' in here and not orderin' anything but I, uh, I um, I didn't bring any money with me."

Liv waved her hand. "Don't worry about it. Stay as long as you want. We're open twenty-four hours. And this is on the house." She pushed the coffee and pie a little closer to him. "It was about to get thrown out anyway," she said with a wink.

The boy smiled sheepishly and took a bite. His eyes shot wide open. Then just as quickly, his brow settled into a deep furrow as he devoured the pie in less than a minute.

Liv chuckled. "Are you studying to be a magician or something? I have never seen a human person make a piece of apple pie disappear so quickly! Can I get you another one of those?"

The boy turned bright red. "No thank you, ma'am. I best be gettin' outta here." He closed his laptop and stuffed it into his backpack. "I thank you kindly for the pie," he said and slid out of the booth just as a large group of rowdy college kids poured into the diner.

The boy buried his chin in his chest and wove through the crowd. He was almost out when a few guys pushed their way through the door, forcing him back inside.

"Excuse me," he said, trying to get around them.

"Whoa! Look who crawled out from under his rock," a dark-haired guy clad in black leather said with a smirk. His overgrown body and attitude

38

filled the door frame. "Isn't it past your bedtime, little man?" he asked, ruffling the boy's hair.

The other guys laughed loudly, and the girls giggled. She couldn't see his face, but she could tell by the beet red color spreading from his ears to the back of his neck the boy was embarrassed. He squeezed past the guys without saying a word and darted out of the restaurant.

Liv scowled at the boisterous group. A thousand ways to tell off her young man's tormentors ran through her mind as she stepped toward them.

"Look alive ladies!" Tom snapped his fingers at the waitresses, pulling Liv off the fast track to termination. She switched out of revenge mode, turned her frown upside down, and got busy taking orders.

Whoever invented the term déjà vu must have worked the night shift at a diner. The following night was just like the night before, and the night before that. Liv found herself standing before another grumpy old man with her tip-winning smile while he decided between a #12 and a #17. And the young man had returned to his booth, pushing Tom to the edge of a full-blown conniption.

"Enough's enough, Liv. Your little boyfriend can't just keep comin' in here like that. I'm runnin' a business here, not a public library."

She rolled her eyes and headed over to the booth with a cup of coffee.

"How's it going—"

"OH NO!" the boy bellowed as he banged on the laptop keys.

"Oh my. I don't think you wanna do that!"

"The screen just went blank!" Suddenly, he stopped abusing the keyboard and focused his fury on the power button, pressing it repeatedly until it finally shut down.

"Please please please please please," he whispered while his leg bounced up and down with enough force to shake his entire body.

Liv stood there holding the cup of coffee whispering, "please please please please please" along with him. She held her breath as she waited for the computer to power up. In the corner of her eye, she noticed Tom moving toward them, but her menacing glance sent him back behind the counter.

The laptop came back to life and the young man commenced a frenzied cycle of typing and clicking.

"NOOOO!!! It's all gone!" He grabbed fistfulls of his hair and looked up at Liv as a river of tears breached his lower lids. It was like his entire world had shattered. Her heart broke into pieces too.

"Hey, hey, don't do that," she said as the boy sobbed, still gripping his hair tightly. She placed the cup of coffee on another table and sat down across from him. "Maybe I can help. Do you mind if I take a look at it?" she asked and waited for consent the boy was in no condition to give.

Turning the laptop to face her, she quickly but gently typed and clicked and typed and clicked for five minutes. "Ah. There you are." She turned it back around. "Is this what you lost?"

Slowly releasing his hair, he looked at the screen then back at her. "How, how did you, how, how can you—" The boy abandoned his efforts to put a sentence together and stared at the waitress with his mouth agape.

"How do I know how to fix your temperamental computer?" she asked with a sly grin. "I think the better question is how come you don't know how to fix your computer? A smart kid like you should have been able to handle a little problem like that in his sleep."

He shrugged. "I guess I sorta panicked."

"Sorta? You had a complete meltdown, dude."

His cheeks turned bright pink. "I'm sorry for causin' a scene," he said with a furtive glance around at the handful of patrons that had already lost interest. "It's just, my final project is due on Monday and it's like seventy-five percent of my grade. If I fail, I'll lose my engineering scholarship and I'll have to go back home." He shook his head. "My parents'll be so disappointed."

Liv nodded. "Where's home?"

"You ever heard of Macon, Georgia?"

"Sure."

"Well, I'm from a small town not too far from there. Eatonton."

"I could tell from the accent you were from the South, but I had no idea you were so far away from home. Your parents let a fifteen-year-old boy come all the way out here all alone?"

The boy frowned. "I'm sixteen, actually."

She tucked her lips in, trying to suppress a smirk. "My mistake. But that's still awfully young. I'd be a nervous wreck if I was your mother."

"Oh, she is, ma'am! I don't think my mama has slept a full night since I left home in August. And she makes me call her every few hours to tell her I ain't been murdered." He chuckled. "But there was no way they would have allowed me to miss out on this opportunity, even if it means never sleepin' again. They can't afford to send me to college without a scholarship."

"I'm sure they're very proud of you."

"Yes, ma'am, I reckon so. I just hope I can keep it that way."

She gave his hand a pat and scooted out of the booth.

"Um, ma'am—"

"Call me Liv. And what's your name by the way?"

"Elijah—Eli." He cleared his throat. "Um, Miss Liv, I hope you don't mind me sayin', but you should really think about doin' some work with computers. You're real good with 'em."

"Why thank you, Eli. That's a flattering compliment from a kid genius like yourself."

He scowled and turned pink again. "Geniuses don't need waitresses to rescue them from minor computer glitches, I'm 'shamed to say."

"Yeah. You must be a real moron if a dumb waitress had to help you with your fancy computer machine."

His mouth and eyes popped wide open. "Oh, I, uh, I'm uh, I'm sorry! I didn't mean it that way."

Liv giggled. "I'm teasing, Eli. I'm a high school computer science teacher. I work here part-time because my husband and I are saving for a house and teachers' salaries suck big time."

"Now I'm even more ashamed," he said softly. "I've been coming in here for weeks and haven't left you one tip."

"Well, let's see. You've ordered maybe three cups of coffee in all that time. So, at a dollar a piece and twenty percent, you would owe me one dollar, give or take." She laughed.

He lifted his hips and pulled out his wallet from his back pocket.

"Don't you dare give me a dollar, Eli."

"But you're tryin' to buy a house," he whined, as he opened his wallet, his empty wallet. "Oh. I coulda sworn I had a dollar."

"It's all right, sweetheart. Tell you what, you can give it to me tomorrow, if that'll make you feel better."

He nodded and Liv left him to his device. Ten minutes later, she returned with the meatloaf special and placed it on the table next to the laptop.

"Miss Liv, I can't—"

"You can pay me back for this too. Ok?"

"Ok. I promise I will." Tears filled his eyes again, but he blinked them away. Then he made the meatloaf, mashed potatoes, and green beans disappear almost as quickly as the pie the night before.

Eli didn't come back the next night or the night after that. Liv began to worry that his mama's worst fear had come true and her little friend had been murdered. But as the days turned into weeks and the weeks turned into months with no sign of Eli and nothing on the news about a slain college student, she figured he must have failed his finals and lost his scholarship. She prayed he would be all right and that he wouldn't give up on getting his education.

The months turned into years and life turned out much differently than Liv had planned. The job she picked up to make extra money and get ahead became the job she needed to make ends meet and stay afloat.

"Hey, Liv, you mind taking the guy that just came in?" the other waitress asked. "My sitter just called. I gotta go; the baby's running a fever."

"I don't mind a bit, sweetheart. I hope he feels better."

"You're the best." She gave Liv a peck on the cheek and a quick hug and rushed out the door.

Liv filled a glass with ice water and headed over to take the man's order.

"What can I getcha?" she asked the gentleman, placing the glass on the table.

He frowned at the menu he was holding. "I'd really love a meatloaf special," he said as he looked up at her with his beautiful, bright, amber eyes. "But I don't see it on the menu."

"Eli?" She clasped her hand over her mouth.

Smiling ear to ear, he slid out of the booth. And before he was fully upright, she threw her arms around his neck and squeezed the life out of him. They held each other rocking back and forth like they were dancing to a slow song only they could hear.

"I can't believe this," Liv said, finally releasing him. "What happened to you? Did you fail your exams?"

"No ma'am. I did real well on my finals, actually," he said as he sat down and gestured to the seat across from him. She obliged. "I'm sorry I never came back. My plan was to go home for the holidays and get a little pick-up job to earn some pocket money for the next semester and so I could pay you back. Unfortunately, my daddy died suddenly right after Christmas. I just couldn't come back. My mama needed me, or maybe I needed her."

Liv held her hand to her heart to keep it from sinking. It didn't work. "I'm sure you needed each other. Oh, Eli, I'm so sorry. Of course you couldn't finish school after losing your dad so suddenly."

"Thank you, Liv, but I did finish. With Daddy's insurance money and a partial scholarship, I was able to go to a school closer to home."

"That's wonderful!" she said, resting her elbow on the table and her chin in her palm. The sudden shift in emotional state made her a bit light-headed, but in a good way. "You have no idea how relieved I am."

"And you have no idea how surprised I am you still work here. I'm in town for a tech conference and I decided on a whim to swing by. I thought maybe someone would remember you and I might get a last name so I could start looking for you on social media. I couldn't believe my eyes when I saw you behind the counter. I guess you really enjoy working here, because you and your husband must have saved enough for a house by now."

She closed her eyes. "My husband passed away about seven years ago."

"Oh, I, I'm so sorry. I had no idea."

She shook her head. "You couldn't have known. But he had been sick for a long time. We had to use our savings and then some for his medical bills. So, the house fell to the bottom of the list of priorities. And with all the debt we accumulated and two kids to raise on my own, somewhere along the way the house just fell off the list entirely, you know?"

He nodded. "My mother-in-law died last year after a long battle with ovarian cancer. Even with excellent insurance, the cost of her medical care was astronomical."

"Wait. Little Eli got married? Do you have kids?"

He chuckled, rubbing his slightly protruding belly. "I don't know about the 'little' part, but yes, we have twin girls." He showed her his cell phone's screensaver.

Liv beamed at the picture of the two little girls with her young man's amber eyes. "Well if you ever wanted to know what you'd look like as a girl, you certainly know now. They're beautiful, Eli." She placed her hand on his.

He placed his other hand on top of the pile and squeezed. "Thank you, Liv."

"Well let me put that meatloaf special in for you! It's not on the menu anymore—the new management wanted to class things up a bit—but the cook keeps a few meatloaves on hand for special guests." She flashed a wink and hurried off to the kitchen before the lump in her throat turned into inevitable tears.

Returning quickly with his dinner, Liv sat and chatted for a few more minutes until more customers came in requiring attention.

"Can I interest you in a cup of coffee and a slice of pie?" she asked Eli as she cleared his dinner dishes.

"As much as it pains me, I'm gonna pass on the pie," he said, patting his belly again.

"How about just a coffee then? We just got one of those machines that makes single servings of coffee. It's the best thing ever. No more wasted pots of coffee!"

A smile spread across his face, morphing quickly into a laugh.

Liv's brow furrowed at his reaction. "We have tea too if you don't like coffee anymore."

"Oh, no! I didn't mean to laugh like that. I just, it's just—" He closed his eyes and took a deep breath. "I'm overjoyed that you are getting good use out of your machine."

She tilted her head at his choice of words. "Well, it's not actually my machine, but I sure do use the hell out of it."

"Liv, sit down please."

Worried, she put the dishes down and slid back into the booth. Eli's expression had gone from smiley to serious in an instant. She said a little prayer he wasn't going to tell her he had a terminal illness or something; she had exceeded her lifetime limit on receiving that kind of news.

"I owe you my life, Liv."

"Come on, Eli, don't you think you're being a little dramatic. I gave you a slice a pie and a meatloaf dinner."

"You don't remember, do you?"

She narrowed her eyes. "Remember what?"

"Fixing my computer."

"I remember that. It was nothing, Eli. Really. You needed help; I was happy to do it."

A smile pulled at the corners of his mouth. "Ever since I found out what a star was I wanted to work for NASA. I saw every movie and read every book about space I could get my hands on, and I was in just about every space-related science club within a thirty-mile radius of my small town—much to my parents' annoyance. But they always managed to scrape together any membership fees and drive me to meetings. They were great."

Liv nodded, having raised a son obsessed with film-making, there was always a club he just had to join or a class he just had to take. Not to mention all the homemade feature films she had been forced to star in over the years. But it all paid off. He had just started working for a small production company and couldn't be happier.

"Anyway, the project you helped me recover was the coding for an intricate heating system that could be used on the International Space Station. I had worked on it all semester, but that night I cracked the code, as it were, and then my computer crashed, followed quickly by my brain—and all my dreams."

Liv pursed her lips. "Eli—"

"I know, I know. But I was only sixteen. Every setback was an insurmountable tragedy back then."

She nodded. "I'm familiar. I have two grown children. I thank my lucky stars every day that we all survived the terrible teens."

He covered his face with his hand. "Don't remind me; I have twin girls," he groaned.

"So, whatever came of your 'intricate heating system?'" she asked with a giggle.

"Well, I got a patent and eventually sold it."

Liv's eyes shot wide open. "To NASA!?"

"No, I'm afraid they weren't interested. I ended up selling it to a private company to use in their new coffee maker—their new single-serve coffee maker."

Liv's jaw dropped. "Are you serious?"

"Yes, ma'am."

"Wow," she said, still gob-smacked. "That's amazing, Eli! I, I don't even know what else to say. So, what's the coffee business like?"

He chuckled. "I have no idea. I traded my coding for cash, stock, and the freedom to pursue interests that fill my soul rather than my pockets. I've been teaching high school computer science for eight years now like this awesome lady I met once—and I love it."

She pressed her hand into her chest again, this time to keep it from exploding from pride. "Well," she said, making no effort to hide the tears sliding down her cheeks. "Let me get you a cup of your coffee, then."

"Our coffee."

Liv was back in a blink and they sat and talked a bit about their families and teaching before she had to tear herself away from her young man and tend to the other patrons. But she carried out her duties feeling like she was floating on air, still high from finding Eli again, or rather him finding her. At the first opportunity, she went to check on him and he was gone. All that was left at his table was the empty coffee cup sitting on top of his receipt. She picked up the cup and the receipt and trudged toward the kitchen with a familiar heaviness weighing down each step.

Suddenly, the cup crashed onto the floor, shattering. Silence fell over the diner as every eye trained on the haggard waitress.

The manager rushed over to her. "Liv! What's wrong?" he asked, holding her up on legs that had turned to jello.

With her mouth hanging open like it had become unhinged, she handed him the receipt. He looked at it, then at her, then back at the receipt, focusing on the tip line and the hand-written note beneath it.

Tip: $250,000.00

Dear Miss Liv,
You are the nicest person I have ever met. Please know that the kindness
you showed me all those years ago meant more to me than I could ever
express. I trust this token of my appreciation will cover the tips I owe you
and any interest that has accrued over the last fifteen years.

Forever your grateful friend,
Eli

Laura Shovan

BAKING SOURDOUGH

"Sourdough Hands: How Bakers and Bread Are a Microbial Match,"
–Lindsay Patterson, NPR, November 12, 2018

There are microbes
under my nails, migrants
from the bubbly mix
of yeast, bacteria,
and flour I feed daily.
The soul of every loaf
draws close to me
when I dimple or knead,
when I offer you a taste.
We have an intimate relationship
with bread, the taste
fermented by my body.
Species move from the dough
to my hand, from my hand
to your mouth, a fluid boundary
between body and bread.
When I put my hands on you,
fungi record the story
of hunger and rising.

Kim Roberts

FROMAGERIE

This cheese tastes like the slant of autumn sunshine on drying hay, and behind that, a hint of old socks.

That cheese tastes tannic, like spring water over last year's leaf mold; it pairs well with red wine that tastes of mung beans and oiled cabretta.

This cheese tastes like the dance of a plover along the selvage of a tide line on a cloudless afternoon.

That cheese blushes with pleasure, then lies down and cries.

This cheese is dusty as a counting house, with a hint of turmeric slipped into a cotton handkerchief.

That cheese rattles like an anchor chain, promising distant ports.

This cheese has a finish of dominoes and faded vanilla.

That cheese is washed clean as two girls recovering from a paroxysm of giggles.

June Forte

WEIGHING IN ON WEIGHTING IN

I really don't know what I weigh. I know what I should weigh, what I used to weigh, and what I plan to weigh, but I really don't know what I weigh.

Is it the number that shows up on the scale in the morning when I'm wearing my pajamas and slippers, and before I empty my bladder? Is it the number the nurse at the doctor's office recorded, when I was wearing my winter coat and carrying my purse–the big one?

It could be the number on my driver's license; or the number I gave when I boarded the prop plane for that scenic flight over the Grand Canyon last summer. Or perhaps it's the guesstimate I entered in the Body Mass Indicator calculator where I also stretched my height–by two inches.

I seem to weigh less in the smoky mirror at the fine Italian restaurant, and more in the one at the local pizza parlor–even if I visit both on the same day. I also look larger in the fitting-room mirror at the thrift store than I do in dressing-room mirrors at the upscale stores in town.

Do I weigh more or less at high altitudes? How about at sea level? Do I weigh more coming off a holiday weekend, and less on Wednesday? Do workouts at the fitness center add muscle weight or do they shrink fat cells? Is weight affected by what month it is? I seem seems to weigh more on January 1 and less in the heat of the summer.

I'm pretty sure I weigh less when I'm at the back of the group selfie and more when I take the selfie for the group. I also weigh less when I pose sideways next to people who stand facing the camera.

There is too much to factor in to get to a scientifically accurate weight. Are all those numbers right at their moments in time, or are they all wrong?

The weight that seems to be the most correct is the one the scale displays when I'm naked, having just removed my earrings, cut my toenails, and pushed my hand down on the countertop--for balance, of course.

What about you? Do you know what you weigh?

George Merrill

WAITING

I've spent much of my life waiting, though each wait had an unusual twist. My sailing days come immediately to mind. I'm a lifelong sailor.

Any sailor navigating the Chesapeake Bay knows how it goes. It's something like this: One day there's a fair breeze. Expectations are high, as my wife and I weigh anchor, set sail and glide down the creek. From Broad Creek we sail into the Choptank River and head out for the Chesapeake Bay. It's mid-August and the summer heat is murderous. The breeze helps some.

In about an hour the breeze shifts a little, becomes erratic and then stops. We swelter in the heat. The wakes of passing motorboats cause us to roll and pitch. The rigging begins arrhythmic slapping against the mast, protesting our delay, while gulls and butterflies glide effortlessly past the boat as though mocking us.

We're dead in the water. The Bay's glossy surface looks torpid and viscous for miles around. My world has simply stopped.

Then, on the distant horizon, I see a long line; it's unmistakable. Behind the line the water is darker and appears troubled, as though shivering or perhaps herring are running just below the surface. No, there's a breeze out there. Coming our way? Yes, and, we wait. Even the murderous heat can't draw our attention from the line that moves with agonizing hesitancy, but inexorably in our direction. The water grows darker as the breeze draws closer. Soon the sails flutter, the rigging grows taught, and I hear the hollow rush of the hull as it slices through the water.

The waiting is over ... for now.

I am an octogenarian, eight score and five, to be precise. I wonder about the measure of my days. How many are left, I think to myself? Just how will they will end? I wait to see.

I am also a man living in the midst of a lethal pandemic, unprecedented in modern history. In stores, I stand in long lines, masked like a robber, and always six feet from others, and I wait. I also wait for COVID-19 to end, but uncertain what the ending might look like. At times I feel as though I'm living my life like the person who sits waiting in an emergency room. He hopes for the best and fears the worst. In any case I wait expectantly. I've been waiting, in one way or another, my whole life. In life, standing and waiting is the name of the game. And there are all kinds of waiting.

The etymology of the word "wait" suggests that over time it's carried mixed messages for us, or more likely, we've mixed its messages. Its early meaning communicated that "one waits with hostile intent," like "you better watch out." It seems to have morphed over time assuming a different tone, the state of being awake or alert. It has evolved to mean generally either to stand by in attendance (serve) or to endure.

Few of us like to wait. There's the universal sense bred in us that we need "to get on with it." In our "now" generation, waiting is not cool. The express lane is where it's always best to queue up.

I've known a kind of waiting that is troubled by the inconsistences inherent in what the waiting's about, times when I'm sitting and wishing for two things at once, wishes wholly incompatible with each other. I'm thinking of that day being with my mother. It would be the last day I would ever be with her.

I'd driven from Connecticut to New Jersey, where my mother was staying with my sister. Terminally ill, my mother's end was near and I wanted to be with her to share in some of her waiting. It was early June, warm and sunny. I sat by her bed where she dozed off and on. A copy of the New York Times crossword puzzle lay beside her. She had done them daily as long as I could recall. She'd just figured out a word. She penciled it in, looked dreamily pleased with herself before putting it aside and nodding off.

The window was half open. A sheer curtain hung there and the sunlight illuminated the translucent images of butterflies imprinted on it. The curtain rose and fell with the light breeze, creating the illusion of oversized butterflies dancing at the windows. My mother and I talked, circumstantially, neither of us really speaking our minds, but I was there to wait, not necessarily to talk.

As I waited I kept trying to square two thoughts, feelings really, neither one remotely in accord with the other. As waves of grief fell over me I knew I did not want to let her go. And still, I wanted her to go, to die. The two-year bout with cancer had ravaged her body and although she remained remarkably good-natured through all the indignities and pain of a lingering illness, I wanted her suffering to end. I felt guilty as if by even entertaining such a thought––wanting her death––I was betraying her. This time of waiting for me was not governed by anything that made sense or what was best. It was governed by the primal ache that arises when we have to confront the most painful of all human realities; that day when we will have to surrender those we love.

As I've thought about it, her waiting was much more single-minded than mine. I knew she'd had enough and was ready to go. Her illness had prepared her for what was inevitable and so she was able to face her future at that moment with less turmoil than I was. Life was still holding pleasures for me that constitutionally she would no longer be able to have. She knew it. I had then no idea of her world. All I could do was wait a while with her and try to access my love for her amid my own inner turmoil.

Sometimes waiting is just plain waiting and it's a pure joy. It's all about anticipation.

As a child in the 1940s––long before Amazon Prime––I remember how receiving mail was a big deal. During WWII, I received V-Mails, letters from my father serving with the Army in the European theater. What lent the letters their allure and peculiar mystique were the words that always preceded the salutation: "Somewhere in Europe." The fact that his whereabouts had to be kept a secret only added mystery to his already heroic stature, as I imagined him the mighty warrior on a foreign battlefield.

These were also the days when I sent a quarter and a Kellogg's cereal box top to the cereal manufacturer to receive my Secret Decoder Ring. What the secret was that the ring decoded is lost to history. I remember only that I wanted one desperately.

I sent my box top and quarter off to get my ring. Anticipating the mail each day was almost painful in its anticipatory promise. And one day the ring came in the mail. I haven't the vaguest notion today how the ring looked; what's indelible in my mind is the energy I felt daily in anticipating the promise that each day's mail held for me.

I suppose now, as I'm living well into my days as an octogenarian, this has highlighted for me the business of waiting. The wait for my end is growing shorter, but the time remaining is deep and rich. Depth is more my preoccupation now than duration. With a trove of experiential treasures behind me––some seemed hardly treasures at the time––still I can assemble the mixed pieces of so many of my past "waitings" into a collage, and weave a tissue of significance from them. My eyes are not as good as they once were, but I know I see a lot more clearly than I did forty years ago. I used to be nearsighted. Now I'm hind-sighted.

I think I now understand why I've spent so much of my life often impatient with most forms of waiting I've had to endure. It's because I never really understood how nothing is ever really finished, nor had I grasped just how tentative life really is. That anything is really over is one of the illusions we create in our ignorance. One act ends, but the play resumes. Becoming continues on in its evolutionary trajectory, just as you and I have. Think of it--from the Milky Way, to pond scum, to primates, to homo sapiens, and arriving where we are today, and even now we keep on going.

Matter, science tells me, is neither created nor destroyed, only transformed. I like to think that's the case with my spirit, too.

"Dear friends," writes the author the Bible's First Epistle of John: "Now we are children of God, and what we will be has not yet been made known."

This much has been made known, for sure. I'll have to wait to find out.

Catherine Carter

BOAT-WOMAN, ST. MARY'S CITY

in memory of Lucille Clifton

You blessed the boats at the sacred
river where I too once was bathed
and blessed; you came the year after
I left, to my regret. So there
is where I imagine you now, though
you've gone further out in that broad
reach than any vessel I've piloted yet;

there, where I imagine the spring peepers
in that muddy pond begin to trill
won't you celebrate with me that every
day someone had again failed to kill
you, or the turtles, risen from mud,
may open their deep throats to croak
forth *these hips have never been enslaved*;

yes, there, where I imagine that by
that river-glitter shining beyond fame or fear
we might meet at last; there where, only
there, I could testify to one more
of us whom your never-enslaved words
set free to sail after you, out
there among the rolling stars' slow swells.

Michael D. Jones

FREEDOM IN A TIME OF REPRESSIONS

Either you want it or you don't.

Freedom
Eludes
The
Authorities.

Freedom
Dances
Between
Us.

Freedom
Either you want it or you don't.

Nina L. Phillips

A CHRISTMAS SURPRISE

"Irushka, wake up!" The shrill cry of my beloved amah, my Chinese nanny, pierced the morning's stillness and woke me up from an unsettled sleep.

I was thirteen years old in January 1939 in Hangzhou, China and I was warmly nestled in my large comfortable bed safe in my spacious bedroom. Home for the holidays. Away from my boarding school, my friends, the nuns, and, gratefully, all my studies.

The Japanese Imperialist Forces had just conquered Hangzhou, but, as Russian allies, we thought we had nothing to fear from the invasion. An uneasy calm had settled over the White Russian community.

My White Russian parents had fled Russia during the Russian Revolution of 1918. The White Russians, who supported the tsar, the Russian Orthodox Church, and the old Russia had bitterly fought the Red Communist Russians, who despised the tsar, the church and embraced a new Russia, and utopia for the working class. But we lost the bloody civil war that pitted brother against brother and the Communists won.

When my uncle, an elite soldier in the Tsarist Guard, was murdered by the Communists, the brave trio (my grandmother, aunt, and mother) fled their beloved Russia. They traveled on the Trans-Siberian Railway like so many White Russians and headed east to China, the ancient mysterious country of the Great Wall, Confucius, and calligraphy. My family joined the thousands of other White Russians, who became Harbin Russians, building the small Chinese town into the city of the largest Russian community outside of Russia.

My parents, Zinaida and Nicholas, married in Harbin and I was born in 1925. I was a twin, but my twin died; even then at my birth, I was a survivor in life. I had a happy early childhood surrounded by my extended family--my grandmother, Aunt Sophie, Uncle Nikolai, and my annoying cousin Stefan. "Good morning, granddaughter," my babushka every day cheerfully addressed the large picture of me hanging in her ornate closet. My father was gone frequently on business; consequently, my mother and I were inseparable. Mom was beautiful, an accomplished baker, and a prolific linguist of Russian, French, English, and some German. My favorite memory was when she read to me classic Russian writers-Pushkin, Gogol, and of course, Tolstoy. "Mon cherie, shall we read the great Gogol tonight?" My mother addressed me in French, the language of Russian aristocracy.

"Mamushka! Gogol! Yes." I reached behind me and retrieved the large book on the bookshelf emblazoned with Nikolai Gogol.

Gogol was a very difficult writer for a small child to comprehend, but I was focused on my mother--her elegant clothes, her sweet smell and gentle voice.

"I have a surprise for you tonight," she continued. "A letter from your father. He says we are taking a boat ride to join him in Hangzhou."

"Will Babushka and Aunt Sophie come also?" I excitedly asked.

"No, they will remain here in Harbin," she replied. "Now time to go to sleep, my angel."

Next week with many tears, our family sadly waved goodbye to us. As I was nine years old, an impending boat ride seemed like so much fun. After all, I would meet my dad at the boat dock and we would be a family again! I was so excited that I could not wait to see him.

"May I go outside and get some fresh air?" I asked my mom, who had a headache in our small cabin.

"Yes. Do not go too far from our room," my mother replied.

I explored the ship on my own, for the ride proved to be most interesting, even entertaining to some extent. In the middle of the boat sat the opium addicts, who ate fruit and smoked their long opium pipes. At one point, a very old Chinese man stood up slowly and painfully on his emaciated body. Turning to look at me, I was horrified at his gaunt yellow face with two dark sunken eyes. I immediately went to find my mother, who was still at rest in her cabin. That was the end of my solo escapades around the ferry.

"Koia! Koia!" My mother delightfully called my dad by his nickname, as he twirled her around with his hands on her small waist. My parents were very much in love. This was a happy season for the three of us in Hangzhou, a beautiful coastal city at the base of the Yangtze River. Many years ago, foreign nations colonized the city and divided it into foreign concessions, like the

French Concession or the Russian Concession. A successful businessman, dad built homes in both the French and Spanish concessions. He was well respected in the community; our international connections would prove to be very valuable for us in the future. At night after dinner, mom and dad would spend time together in the gazebo outside our main home, drinking their tea and discussing their hopes and dreams.

What I liked best was the picnics on the Fuchun River. We found a special place for our boat, where the shore met the land with the lush green trees behind us and we ate food with our friends. My dad played songs on his guitar and sang with his best friend, Mr. Aristiti, who enthusiastically chimed along in his native Greek. The Chinese fisherman even showed us how to catch shrimp. What a delicious treat!

I attended St. Mary's Boarding School with girls of many different nationalities--French, Italian, German, Russian, and even a few American. I really enjoyed my monthly skating trips with my friends. Dressed all in black, the nuns wore a very traditional habit that had many petticoats. I hoped the nuns would skate, so I could count them all, but they never did. When I was sick, I went home, crawled in bed with my mom and read the Russian classics. My mom's health was declining; somehow, I always thought that she would get better.

One day, I walked with my father down the main boulevard of Hangzhou. West Lake, a lake in the heart of the city, had inspired Chinese poets and painters for centuries with its natural beauty of waterfalls, soft green trees, and colorful exotic flowers.

It was a cloudless warm day and the trees that majestically lined the boulevard smelled sweetly of the season. My father, as always, was impeccably dressed in a black suit with a white handkerchief in his lapel. When he greeted a female, he kissed their hand; women loved that charming European gesture.

I was very proud to be his daughter--his precious princess. As we strolled past the busy city life (merchants with commodities, food vendors, and the occasional beggars), my father protectively clutched my hand and kept me close to him.

Suddenly, we heard a loud buzzing noise above us and we simultaneously looked up to the sky.

"That is a Soviet plane," my father quietly said.

I looked up with curiosity at the solo plane above us. "Do you mean all the way from Russia? Why is it here?"

"Stalin has made 'friends' with the Japanese here in China," my father sarcastically stated, and we watched the plane as it disappeared.

"Don't worry, little one! It is nothing! We should eat ice cream and not think about Soviet planes! It's too lovely of a day to waste!" My dad reassured me, but his grip on my hand was tighter and his voice was tense.

Despite my dad's outward calm demeanor, I had not forgotten that single Soviet plane. That night I had a nightmare: The plane multiplied to thousands and they decended into our peaceful life like a swarm of black locusts.

My mother died from heart disease when I was just thirteen years old. My best friend had died, and I was inconsolable. In the Russian tradition, mom was placed downstairs in the main living room, so the Russian Orthodox priest could administer the last rites to her. The servants covered the entire house in black all over the windows, doors, and tables. Many people came to our house to pay their last respects, yet I stayed alone in my room. My amah and dad were very concerned, because I also completely stopped eating food.

Later, dad bought beautiful black marble for her headstone with a weeping willow tree planted over her grave. Both were especially imported to China–the weeping willow tree, not indigenous to China, the only one in the entire city. In my bedroom as the rain tapped on my window, I thought about my mom, the black marble, and the weeping willow tree. Although they were beautiful tributes to my mother's memory, nothing could ever heal the hole in my heart from her death.

"Iruska, I think it will be a good idea to sleep in our clothes," my dad said to me at breakfast weeks later. He put his paper down and looked seriously at me.

"Our clothes? Do I need to wear my shoes, too?" I looked over my oatmeal at him.

My dad sighed. "No. Don't forget tonight."

I understood immediately, because a friend was arrested in his pajamas last week in the middle of the night by Stalinist police. My dad did not want that indignity to happen to us. When his French friends visited us one evening, they invited us to move to the safety of their concession. "I am not a political man. Iruska and I will be fine," dad told them in our living room. Somehow, I do not know why he believed that, since of course he was a political man.

He was, after all, the president of the White Russian Association; therefore, he was on Stalin's hit list.

One night, I was in a peaceful sleep in my bed and the worst happened. My dad came quietly in my room and looked down on me as I slept. His solemn white face hovered over me like a bright iridescent moon in a dark starless night.

"We have company," he said. The Chinese police officially took us away, but we knew Stalin's secret police were behind the evil deed. Separated from my dad, I was taken to a small room where a large imposing Chinese woman sat behind a desk. "Give me your arm," she curtly stated, while she prepared to tattoo me with a prison number. Suddenly, she stopped, and put down her tools with a compassionate look at the terrified young woman in front of her.

"You will grow up to be a beautiful young woman. I will put the tattoo up here on your upper arm," she said. For me, this was a defining moment in my life--I never forgot, even in the worst and most unlikely places, there can be human kindness and goodness in people.

Some White Russians committed suicide in prison, while some just disappeared totally off the face of the Earth. My dad and I were the lucky ones. After word got out about our arrest, our French friends negotiated our release just a month later. Since all our property was seized by the government, we returned to the French Concession to start a new life. My dad resumed his business and our fortunes dramatically changed for the better. Our life again entered some new normalcy for my dad at work and me at school.

The Christmas season of 1939 was a special time of hope and new promise for the New Year. Miraculously, we survived the Russian Communist prison camp while so many poor souls never returned. Now our huge home in the French Concession was a place of safety and restoration for both of us. Even the recent conquest of Hangzhou by the Japanese Imperialist forces could not derail our holiday joy.

"We have no quarrel with the Japanese. They will leave us alone." My father, president of the White Russian Association, assured his anxious friends and colleagues. Still sometimes, even under his positive demeanor, I thought I saw a hint of fear in his deep blue-violet eyes.

It was hard not to notice the Japanese presence in our town. The Imperial Japanese Army headquarters was across the street from our palatial home.

Their Rising Sun flag flew conspicuously over us, with its red circle on the white cloth like a large blood stain on frozen snow.

I missed my friends from St. Mary's Boarding School, and I had a special bond with several Russian Jewish girls, who were political refugees like me. That was behind me, as I celebrated my Christmas holiday with my loving father and devoted amah in our luxurious sixteen-room mansion with the large portraits of the tsar and tsarina in the entrance.

After my mother's death, my amah's love filled a- deep void in my heart. Our servants lived in the other side of our house and, of all our help, she was the most special to me. My father even attempted to matchmake her with one of his construction workers.

With a wink, he told her, "Don't forget now. He's waiting for you-he would make a good father for your daughter." Amah said nothing to him, as blushing, she continued, with a smile, to her busy duties.

Now I jumped out of my bed and put on my heavy warm robe this chilly Hangzhou morning. As I wiped the sleep from my eyes, I followed my amah down the stairs past the hall decorated festively for Russian Christmas-- garlands of dried fruit, fragrant pine wreaths, and presents under the tall Christmas tree. Amah's very diminutive bound feet pranced quickly ahead of me across the shiny parquet wood floors to the front door.

"Look!" my amah ceremoniously announced and opened the door with excitement. On the ledge of the door and on the steps were scattered amazing presents--candies, Japanese books, and canned fruit. We dove into the assorted gifts like an unopened treasure chest at the bottom of the ocean.

Amah picked up the most precious gift--a lovely, small Japanese doll. She was dressed in a purple kimono and her china doll arms sat limply at her side. Her life-like eyes blinked in the new morning light as if to say hello to her new owner.

Of course, my surprise benefactor was our neighbor across the street. This was a touching gesture, for the Japanese military forces were not known particularly for acts of kindness towards others, especially in occupied China. As a child, I had heard of Japanese atrocities in my birth city of Harbin. When the poor helpless Chinese fled on the frozen river, the Japanese trapped them and turned the crystal ice palace into a crimson grave.

My father was delighted with the surprise gifts. "Can you believe this, Iruska?" he excitedly asked me, as he looked over the multitude of presents. "Which one is your favorite?"

"The doll, of course! I'll name her Vera, after my best friend!" I picked up my little Japanese doll and kissed her on the cheek.

"Vera, it is! What a wonderful Christmas surprise! I will send them a special gift for their generosity to you!" My father beamed with happiness.

Immediately, as a thank you, he sent a case of vodka to the headquarters. The Japanese loved children and I looked much younger than thirteen years old. Now we already had favor with them; this was a good reassuring sign to my family.

Our peaceful co-existence with the Imperial Japanese Army headquarters was short-lived. Less than a year later we received another surprise "gift" from our new neighbors. Posted to the same door, the very official brief notice stated that we had forty-eight hours to evacuate our beautiful home.

Iruska and Vera, the doll, both safely left China in January 1949 and became permanent residents of the United States Eastern Shore.

Donna Rothert

NOTHING OF INSIGNIFICANCE

Sitting on the foyer floor, Kate Monroe felt her frustration rising, the familiar burn starting low in her abdomen, working its way past her chest, slowly climbing to her throat, burning, burning. Why had she offered to help Emily when she barely knew her? Wait, that was not quite accurate. She knew a lot about Emily--where she had grown up, her childhood accomplishments and disappointments, her relationships with her siblings, even her artistic ambitions.

Kate had met Emily months earlier at a weekly workshop, "Writing Your Memoir", facilitated by a local author who had just published her own life story. And during those workshops, Kate had listened to the arc of Emily's life as she described her childhood to adolescence. Sadly, too often the workshop sessions disintegrated into protracted readings by bitter souls seeking sympathy for their tales of injustice, criticism, and imagined offense. But Emily had seemed different, more thoughtful, more satisfied, and her writing bordered on the lyrical. So, during the mid-morning break, when Emily mentioned that she was going through a divorce and would soon be moving from the family home into a local condo, Kate had offered a few hours of her time to help with the packing and schlepping of lightweight boxes. Kate herself had been divorced for years and knew the stress could be overwhelming.

On this January Thursday, Kate found herself sitting on the hardwood floor at the foot of the stairs in Emily's foyer. As she looked around, she realized she was in trouble and should have made an excuse when she first arrived, feigning either illness or a forgotten dentist appointment.

To the left was a living room where no living had occurred for years. The space was crammed with towering piles of plastic boxes, some empty, most full, piled under and over other cardboard boxes, a few from the local liquor store, giving Kate hope that Emily would take an occasional drink to calm her nerves. There were hundreds of makeshift containers, anything with a bottom and sides that could hold "stuff," most purchased, some gifted, all excessive, providing safe harbor for clones, duplicates, and facsimiles. Why have only one item if you can have forty-three? In this maze, Kate recognized Quaker oatmeal cylinders, metal coffee tins, abandoned jewelry boxes, shoe boxes, baskets, and hundreds of plastic bags emblazoned with the names of local retailers--Target, Pier One, Harris Teeter, CVS, Marshall's.

At the opposite end of the room, five shelves of built-in bookcases suffered the weight of DVDs, figurines, vases, dried flowers, CDs, pens and pencils, notebooks, and even a book or two. A small portable TV huddled inside the kneehole of the desk. The living room offered no safe passage. Although a sofa and four chairs hugged the walls--at least Kate thought she glimpsed four chairs--there was no place to sit.

To the right, Kate saw a narrow path leading from the foyer through the dining room to the kitchen, where no countertops were visible under the mass of foodstuffs, dishes, water bottles, and papers including a Baltimore Sun from last month. Scattered notepads, appliance instruction booklets, and lists of never-attempted tasks covered the center island. Around the corner, stacks of books, piled ten to fifteen high, were precariously parked against the window seat just below the bay window. Had these books been banished from the living room bookcases to make room for more decorative items? Kate guessed that not much food preparation occurred in that kitchen and even wondered what might have been stuffed temporarily into the oven and microwave, only to be later abandoned.

In the dining room, hundreds of breakable items—water glasses, wine goblets, china plates, and pottery--infested every flat surface including the windowsills and floor. The credenza and a hutch were crammed with linens and additional china sets, while housing six complete sets of silver cutlery. A small non-working crystal chandelier perched in the corner atop three cardboard boxes, its electric cord wrapped around its stem, two bulbs missing.

So this Thursday morning, Kate found herself sitting cross-legged on the only cleared space available, the foyer floor. Despite her misgivings, Kate had decided to stay, and she watched as Emily began pulling hats from the foyer closet's upper shelves, mostly winter hats, woolen, blacks and browns, promising to warm the head, threatening to destroy the hairdo.

"How many hats do you have?" Kate asked.

"Oh, I don't know," Emily replied as she swept around the growing pile. "There are more upstairs."

Emily was tiny with a short, gray-blonde pixie haircut, porcelain skin, bright azure eyes and a ready smile. Her voice wavered as she spoke, rasping her words from her throat past her lips, not stuttering but somehow tentative, as though her words were probationary, waiting for acknowledgement and even acceptance. Even so, there was a tinge of lemon in her voice.

Kate recalled that when she first offered help, Emily warned that she was a hoarder, but had qualified her statement: "But I am a clean hoarder." When Kate probed further, Emily described her "collecting" as piles of papers, sets of dishes, assortments of photos, the un-organized assemblage of memories from a 32-year marriage. Still, Kate was not prepared for the overwhelming volume of stuff engulfing the home's first floor.

"There are more hats upstairs." Emily glanced hopefully at Kate.

"Well, let's get them all down here so you can make informed decisions," Kate said. "Your job now is to find every hat you own and bring them here."

"First, I need a bottle of water," Emily deflected. Kate soon learned this was Emily's tactic to delay the inevitable. For Emily, decisions were hard, if not impossible, threatening her with an uncomfortable finality, no matter how trivial or insignificant.

Fifteen minutes later, after multiple trips to upstairs bedrooms, the pile had grown to ninety-two hats--straw, brimmed, fedoras, berets, bonnets, even a cowboy hat, mostly muted colors, with an occasional hot pink or cerulean blue whimsy thrown in the mix. In what would become her routine, Emily plucked each hat from the pile, slowly caressing and inspecting it, conjuring all the reasons it should go into the "keep" pile. Kate hoped the hat corral would be an easy place to start. "After all," she thought, "how much attachment can you have to a hat?"

Mustering her calmest voice, Kate set down the first rule. "You do not need ninety-two hats, Emily. You may keep ten."

Although arbitrary, Kate felt "ten" was reasonable and knew she had to start strong. This reduction rule would become the foundation for any progress that day or in the coming weeks. A stack of 142 picture frames? You can keep twenty. A pile of 714 audio cassettes? You can keep fifty. There was neither rhyme nor reason to Kate's required percentages, just an inexorable winnowing of "too many."

Kate sympathized that Emily had suffered a painful childhood with an unavailable mother and bullying siblings and was now struggling with an acrimonious divorce. The marital animosity became glaringly evident within minutes of Kate's arrival that first day, when Emily's husband, Malcolm, poked his shaggy, bearded face around the corner to carp about their hat-sorting activity.

"Em-i-LEEEE" he whined, "do you HAVE to put all those hats on the floor? What if I need to get to the front door to get out? What if there's a fire?" Kate considered retorting "What if you need to get to the kitchen?" but thought better of it.

Of average height, Malcolm's hunched-over posture made him appear even smaller, beaten down, shuffling through the kitchen and dining room with neither energy nor purpose, eyes downcast. Over the next several months, Emily would remain the target of his sing-song, obscure criticism.

Kate sat patiently, hunched over the pile of hats on the foyer floor in the two-story brick colonial, on a heavily treed lot of oaks and maples, backing onto lush open space—prime real estate in that Maryland community. Kate worried that helping Emily would require digging deep into her own shallow well of patience. She began to think of this activity as an exercise in psychological karate. She needed to disable Emily's deep-seated hoarding habits while at the same time building up her confidence and self-esteem.

Kate, whom everyone considered organized, knew how to get results, worshiping at the altar of the Four Piles of Decluttering--Keep, Sell, Donate, Recycle/Trash. She would soon learn that Emily would need to add two more piles: Gifts I Once Bought to Give to Friends and Still Need To as well as Items I Bought for My Son Jack but Never Gave Him. Not a good sign.

"Oh, but I like the color of this one, such a pretty rose" or "Look at this cute kitten on the hat brim." Emily pleaded for each hat, cap, beanie. A color or a memory or a family gift or an unreasoned "but I like it" constituted her persistent defense. Every hat was important.

Kate took a breath and in her gentlest tone, repeated "Emily, you can keep ten hats--only ten--and donate the rest for others to enjoy." Kate watched Emily's face fall and then slowly transition to a fragile determination suggesting she would be able to do this ... maybe ... hopefully ... with help.

Over the next few weeks, Kate would return to the colonial on the lovely lot, always limiting her assistance to two hours, for the magnitude of the task had become emotionally overwhelming. Emily's devoted attachment to things was the anchor for her personality. Kate realized Emily feared she might actually disappear without the physical evidence that she had lived, that she had travelled to Japan, that she had listened to CDs, that she once married and had a son, that she had cut out important articles to read later. Nothing was insignificant, not paper clips or broken pencils or inkless pens. Emily needed to touch each item, tell how each became part of her life, and finally evaluate its usefulness or beauty or value as a memory trigger.

The next few weeks, Kate was reduced to repeating the rules and covertly slipping broken items into the trash pile before Emily began describing all the ways she could fix things. According to Emily, she had scores of friends for whom she had bought gifts, never delivered but now ready. Kate thought Emily would need to live to be 110 in order to glue all the china, read all the saved articles, and frame and hang all the artwork she wanted to keep.

Kate also knew she served as a buffer to Malcolm's incessant criticism and whining as he hovered in the next room. What had started as an innocent offer to help someone during a difficult time had left Kate frustrated and irritable, often admonishing Emily to "Pay attention. Stay focused. You do not need forty-six eight-by-ten wooden picture frames. You do not have that much wall space." And Emily would comply, temporarily, only to return to her routine of touch, remember, evaluate.

For several days, they continued to catalogue their way through the center of the living room. One day Kate turned to a five-foot-tall Regency walnut bachelor's chest on the south wall, its five serpentine drawers sitting atop four clawed feet. Kate, knowing full well what the answer would be, asked "Is that chest already emptied?"

"Oh no," said Emily, "I am sure it is full." And to Kate's dismay it was— filled with greeting cards, most bought and never sent, folded and faded, gaudy and glittered, and by Kate's estimate numbering more than 600. Quick calculations at $3 per card, a conservative average over the last twenty years, and the unopened contents of that bachelor's chest equaled nearly $1,800 in wasted opportunity.

Kate, sapped of every drop of patience, turned to Emily, sitting across the room happily sorting through ancient audio cassettes and mumbling tales of why each was her favorite.

"Do you know how many greeting cards you have here? You could start your own Hallmark store. Have you ever thought of the time and money wasted when these cards were stored and then ignored for years?"

Emily looked up, hurt. "I don't think about it at the time. And I told you I was a hoarder. This isn't helpful."

And suddenly Kate remembered that, yes, Emily had warned her. And then surprisingly, she remembered her former husband's piles of paper, piles upon pile, and collections of books, stacked on the floor and tables throughout their small apartment during the early years. And how "stuff" continued to accumulate, relentlessly, even after they moved into a much larger home in the suburbs. Kate had almost forgotten the unending clutter, buried the memory deep. And now she wondered if her offer to help Emily was a counterfeit penance for her inability to save her marriage, to clear the physical and emotional disarray of their lives. No time to think about it now.

Kate pressed on, frustrated after weeks of biting her tongue, deflecting Malcolm's snarky comments, and bolstering Emily's confidence for imperceptible progress.

"Doesn't this make you mad? Or at least sad? Money spent on these cards could have been a trip to Paris off-season. Or a week in Florida last winter when it was so horribly cold and stormy."

Across the room, Emily became smaller, teared up, and refused to answer.

Drained, Kate knew she had to leave and that she could not return. She had hoped to help, and she had in some ways, but Emily's patterns were too deep-seated, her world view too narrow, her emotion too raw. Progress had been made. Kate had to admit that. But Emily was still months from getting the house presentable for sale.

As she headed for the door, Kate turned, admonishing Emily as gently as possible.

"Look, you have made good progress here over the last two months. And I want you to channel my voice and questions as you continue to get rid of your stuff. You've certainly heard me enough. Let me know how you're doing and good luck!" And she meant it.

In April, Kate visited Emily's new condo, helping her unload bulky rugs from her small SUV, into the newly painted and freshly washed condo. It was a lovely ground-floor unit with floor-to-ceiling windows opening onto a small patio, just the size for a small table and two chairs. It bordered a park.

But Kate was saddened to see that already the ghosts of accumulation and indecision had permeated every single inch of what could have been Emily's fresh start.

While they continued to text each other, Kate knew she could not face the condo's re-creation of the gathering of objects as a cure for loneliness, just in a smaller space.

Then in early June, she received a long text from Emily, "We have a family coming to see the house on Saturday!!! But I have not made enough progress. Malcolm and I both marveled at how effective you were working with me. Would you be able to help me for a bit tomorrow going through my stuff? I already have donated a ton but need to do much more."

Kate demurred at first but offered two hours the following week, selfishly curious as to the progress Emily had made.

Kate had come to believe her sympathy for Emily stemmed from Kate's own parents, who had lived through the Depression and never threw away anything that could be of use to anyone. After her father had passed, Kate discovered a box of 116 light bulbs in his garage: refrigerator bulbs, oven bulbs, projector bulbs, clothes dryer bulbs, incandescent, fluorescent, halogen, CFL, LED. Kate mused he had probably even saved a bulb that would fit Emily's forsaken dining room chandelier. But where her dad had saved functional items from necessity, Emily hoarded from emotional need.

And the more Kate thought about it, the more she wondered about her own failed marriage. Was there a deep emotional need on her husband's part that Kate was unable or unwilling to fulfill? She now admitted she had ignored the clutter and had mustered neither the skills nor the dedication to resolve their issues. And she was sad.

Kate realized she did not know how to deal with Emily's issues either. She could only give her rules, offer her skills, and hope that somehow Emily could channel Kate's voice as she continued room by room, closet by closet. Kate was soon to find out.

Three days later, Kate appeared once more at the front door of the colonial, hoping for clear floors and usable furniture, and she was pleasantly surprised. While some boxes and baskets still hugged the walls of each room, gone were the piles, the bags, the stacked and discarded detritus of a life never quite enough. Malcolm was still shuffling and whining throughout the house, but at least now he could move safely without fear of tripping or falling.

"Wow, this is quite a difference!" she complimented Emily who grinned in response. "What is on the agenda today?"

"Upstairs bedroom closet!" Emily trumpeted, proud that she had graduated from entire rooms to a lone closet.

Having never been on the second floor, Kate feared what she would find. But all floors were clear, boxes neatly stacked, except for the closet, which reminded Kate of the old Fibber McGee closet, which when opened, buried Fibber with its contents. This was not quite as bad. Kate was in no danger, but the closet had no nooks or crannies that had not been filled.

As Emily sat on a small stool, Kate began pulling the boxes, bags, and plastic containers, one by one from the depths. And Emily once again held each item, touching, telling, and evaluating. Used make-up that should have been discarded years before, Emily designated for the donate pile, until Kate reminded her of health restrictions. Multiple gifts for her son Jack, bought for an 8-year-old, Emily relegated to the keep pile in case her 22-year-old might possibly want them. But Kate's final defeat was the eighty-five sets of shoulder pads, some rotted from the heat of too many summers stored deep in that closet. Evidently, decades earlier, Emily had carefully removed each set from fashionable jackets and blouses, and now, thirty years later, proclaimed all the reasons she should keep them. Kate knew now that she was truly done.

She finished up her two-hour commitment and wished Emily well, realizing that while her help might have been a band-aid, Emily needed surgery. As she walked down the sidewalk from the lovely colonial in the Maryland suburbs, she knew she had done her best. And now Kate had to let go of the hope that she could help Emily reduce her reliance on things to boost her self-worth and self-confidence.

Unexpectedly, Kate discovered her offer to help Emily clear out her suburban home filled with stuff helped Kate resolve the quiet guilt she had carried for fourteen years. She had always believed that if she had only been smarter and worked harder, her marriage would have lasted. Now she felt that lingering burden lift as she recognized none of it would have made a difference.

Tara Elliott

HONEYSUCKLE

Petals softer than skin
cup nectar deep & wait
for the precise moment
the tongue tip
touches
the smallest of drops.

I will inch
       along
              wooden fences,
climb over the tops of these trees,
even across the shale. Rooted here
in coolest shade—
I want you
          the way
honeysuckle craves
the sun.

Christine Brennan

SUBURBAN AFFAIRS

Martin spotted them the moment he stepped off the train.

It was Sarah -- surely it was her, with that pricey scarf he'd bought for her 40th and her dark, curly hair gone all frizzy from the humidity like it always did. She had walked up to the taxi queue, to a man who was already standing in line. He was wearing a beige trench coat, the kind Martin always associated with spies slipping through foggy cobblestone alleys on missions for the Resistance. The man--blond, tall--moved his umbrella to shield them both from the rain that had been coming down all day, then bent toward Sarah to say something. She laughed in response. Then they kissed hello like lovers.

A cab, flicking its wipers, pulled up to the curb. The man opened the door and got in first, as he should. Martin had always prided himself on his knowledge of proper etiquette, so when he saw men do this he was usually pleasantly surprised. Manners were such a rarity these days. But he was not pleasantly surprised right now. No, right now, what he was was shocked. Shocked, and disappointed that a man who understood such courtesies would be so disrespectful as to shag someone else's wife.

The taxi pulled away, crimson taillights blurring with the couple's silhouettes in the rear window. It maneuvered into traffic and was gone.

Martin looked around the platform. Had anyone been around, he might have given into the extremely uncharacteristic impulse to grab a stranger's arm and yell, "Did you see that?! That was my wife and some guy she's having an affair with!"

But he was alone. The train that had deposited him here just seconds ago had already departed, as though chagrined on his behalf.

Martin and Sarah's lives first intersected at a small but well-respected liberal arts college in the Northeast. He was two years ahead of her, a double major in finance and economics, and was preparing for graduation at about the same time Sarah was declaring art history as her major. They left university without ever having met.

It was in their early twenties, at an engagement party for mutual friends, that they drifted toward one another and began to chat. Two years later, they were being married in a reception hall with three attendants each and a small jazz trio playing background music (Martin didn't like to dance). At the time, he was a junior analyst at a local insurance firm he'd joined right out of school, and solidly on the management track. Sarah, meanwhile, adored her job as curator of their village's small but edgy art museum.

Around Sarah's 28th birthday, they bought a four-bedroom house in Ryland Acres with the intention of filling it. By the time she was 33, however, it was clear children weren't going to come naturally. This is the way it is for so many people these days, they thought, hurling themselves into the world of fertility research. After the indignity of providing specimens, Martin was given the all clear. Sarah girded for a battery of tests but after single hormone panel the doctor flatly dissuaded them from attempting IVF. "Premature ovarian failure," he said. "It would be a waste of money."

They were, to put it mildly, concussed by the news. They'd always assumed children were part of their future. Gamely, they tried to regroup, discussing the pros and cons of fostering and adoption. They even put Martin's specimens into cold storage in case they decided to pursue surrogacy. But, time went on, and they moved forward on none of those fronts. The lack of decision being, of course, a decision in itself.

Now in their mid-40s, Martin and Sarah moved from one day into the next. Each morning, Martin took the 6:20 a.m. express to the city and his firm, where he was now the director of risk management. As for Sarah, her job had lost its allure not terribly long after the spate of doctor's appointments, and eventually she left it altogether. Her days were now spent working on her garden, binge-watching British TV shows and keeping the too-big house clean.

Until about four months ago.

At first, Sarah was supportive, indignant that after nearly 20 years at the firm Martin had been given "a pink slip". Her archaic term for being fired was quaintly juxtaposed with the rest of her sentence. "Assholes," she fumed, the crassness catching Martin off guard. "After all you've done for them. And with no warning, no notice whatsoever!"

He'd made a vague head motion when she said this, but said nothing. The dismissal wasn't out of the blue. For some time--perhaps since they learned about the infertility, he wasn't quite sure--the ambition that had once coursed through him like a lifeblood had been winnowing. Where he once thrived on spreadsheets and business continuity plans, he was now bored and uninspired, missing deadlines and making small but silly mistakes. His growing apathy was a bit concerning, since it was making its appearance at an inopportune time: his agency had been recently acquired by a global insurance behemoth, one with an irksome red dodo bird as its mascot. A cadre of management consultants had been prowling the halls and meeting behind closed doors for weeks.

Nor could he say he hadn't been warned. Pam Richards, the head of Human Resources, reiterated this point when she called him into the conference room that spring Friday.

"As you know, Mr. Stewart ...," she started, glancing down at a file in front of her. Pam had been installed as the head of HR earlier this year, following the takeover. Had she always called him "Mr. Stewart"? He'd only met her a few times but they were on a first-name basis ... weren't they?

"We've had you on a Performance Improvement Plan--a PIP-- for several months," she continued. "Together, we set several goals. Goals that we both agreed were achievable and essential to your being able to remain on here."

"Yes," Martin said, clearing his throat. "The PIP. Well, it's been ... "

"Unfortunately, you've not been able to reach those goals," she said, talking over him and closing the file. She raised flat, emotionless eyes to look steadily at Martin. "I'm afraid we're going to have to let you go."

He stared at her, dumbstruck.

"Do you understand what I'm saying?" she said into the silence. "I'm sorry to be so blunt, but I want to be clear. We are terminating your employment."

"Termination ... ?" Martin asked, horrified that his tendency to laugh when nervous made him sound amused at the prospect, which he most assuredly was not. "I thought, ... I mean, after all my time here I thought there would be more ..."

"No," she said, cutting him off. "We both know this has been going on for quite some time. The PIP was a last resort."

She slid paperwork across the desk to him. With the dirty work over, her tone softened ever so slightly. "This is a separation agreement, Martin. You have one week to accept these terms, which are quite generous to reflect your years of service. Please come back to me as soon as possible so we can get everything settled."

She picked up the phone on the conference table and dialed a number. A few minutes later, a security guard came in carrying two boxes of Martin's personal effects and escorted him out of the building.

Weeks, then months, slipped by with no new job. Oh, recruiters called initially, but eventually the phone stopped ringing when Martin didn't return their messages. When Sarah would come to him, fretting, he'd wave his hand noncommittally. "We have a decent severance package. Plenty of time to sort things out."

He told her he was networking and looking into things online--and it was true he had been looking. But finding a new job was so daunting these days. It used to be, you sent in your resumé and, if the company was interested in you, they contacted you. Now one could wander aimlessly through The Cloud before seeing something interesting. Then, you'd be confronted by an endless succession of computer screens and drop-down menus and boxes with 50-character limits into which you were supposed to compress your entire career. There was no way to elaborate on your experience, to expand on your value. Midway through the applications he would lose steam and slowly close his laptop.

The real truth, though, was that Martin felt no sense of urgency to secure a new position. He should have been getting more anxious by the day. Instead he was imbued with an inexplicable calmness, a near yogic serenity. All these years of working, all this effort ... for what? What was the point? Midlife crisis, right on cue.

Sarah, he knew, wasn't oblivious to his mindset. Her concern seemed to grow in tandem with his indifference, concern that might be verging on panic now. Her initial optimism about Martin starting his "next chapter" had waned after a month or so, when nothing materialized. She'd begun to quiz him on his progress every morning, often before he'd even poured his coffee. She seemed irritated by his very presence in the house, looking surprised to find him showering at 10 am or snapping at him for minor infractions like forgetting to put the recycling out.

At least, then, though, she seemed aware of him. For the past several weeks, she'd been so distant, aloof. Sometimes she'd stare blankly at him for a few seconds, as if trying to place him, then go back to whatever she'd been doing as though he wasn't there.

She'd also disappeared a few times. He'd think she was in the garden or watching TV only to look out the window and see that her car was gone, though he'd never heard her leave. When she got home, she never offered an explanation, just went back about her business in the kitchen or upstairs. And Martin never asked. He knew that his hanging around the house every day had upset her daily life, her routine. He didn't want to intrude any more on her privacy.

After all, Martin was the sort of man who dutifully went to work every day, five days a week, for twenty years. He took for granted that Sarah did whatever she said she did during the day, and that what she didn't tell him wasn't worth his knowing. He trusted his wife.

Feckless.

Martin lay on the bed, staring at the ceiling and turning the word over in his mind. He'd come across it in a book yesterday and it fairly jumped off the page at him. Is that what he was? He certainly lacked initiative right now, but the word implied something more chronic, and intentional. The way he felt right now was temporary, he was sure of it. And it wasn't intentional. He just needed to find his feck again.

He sighed and brought himself up onto his elbows. He had to do something productive today. Just one thing. His gaze fell on the closet door and thought: Nothing like a spring cleaning to get the old juices flowing again.

Rain hammered the bedroom windows as he went about his task for a good hour. He was examining a blue-and-black striped tie when he heard a car door slam shut. Moving the curtain aside, he looked through the rain-streaked glass to see Sarah's Volvo SUV backing out of the drive.

Before he could think through what he was doing, he tossed the tie onto the bed and hurried downstairs. He drove so infrequently now it took him a few moments to find his keys. He slid behind the wheel of the Honda Civic, the "train car" they purchased just for Martin to go back and forth to the station each day, and impatiently turned the key in the ignition. The somewhat neglected engine sputtered and coughed before it caught.

Although he was just a minute or two behind her, Martin had already lost sight of her. He hesitated at the stop sign, trying to decide which way to go. Peering through the drizzle, he headed downtown, intending to drive past places Sarah might run an errand: the grocery store, the bank, her hair salon.

But as he turned down Royal Oak Road, which skirted the train station, he saw the Volvo in the parking lot.

He jerked the wheel, maneuvering the car into the packed lot, and scanned the aisles for a space. She must have gotten one of the last ones. Finally, a BMW pulled out ahead of him and he impatiently pulled into the spot behind it. He flung the door open, bashing the car next to him by accident. He thought briefly about leaving a note, which of course is what he would have normally done, but reminded himself of his mission and set out on a diagonal jog across the lot.

Panting, he arrived under the station overhang and stood a moment to catch his breath. He looked up to see Sarah striding briskly through the glassed-in bridge to the other side of the tracks. She was going to the city, or at least headed in that direction. He didn't recognize the outfit she was wearing. His head swam. Why was she going to the city in the middle of the day? And without telling him?

A faint thrumming of the rails indicated the approach of the city-bound train. Martin knew from two decades of experience that if he was going to make the train he had about 30 seconds to get to the other side. His legs were moving before he registered his own decision to follow her.

Bolting past the ticket machines and newsstand, he dodged slower travelers like a Formula One driver and took the steps to the crossover bridge two at a time. The train was pulling in. He ran faster. As he descended to the platform on the other side, he stumbled and had to grab the railing to stop himself from tumbling down the rest of the stairs. He hit the platform hard. With just a second to glance to his right, he could see the top of Sarah's head about fifty yards away, in a knot of passengers, moving onto the first car.

"Stand clear of the closing doors please!" a jovial computerized voice announced overhead. Martin had to turn sideways but made it onto the last car just as the doors snapped shut.

The train lurched forward and quickly gained speed. He didn't need to make his way forward; this train was an express with only one place to disembark. Blurred station name signs briefly imprinted in the train windows as they hurtled toward the city. He sat numbly in his seat, waiting. They would arrive, Martin knew, in less than 20 minutes.

As the train entered a tunnel on its final approach, the car darkened. Brakes squeaked and hissed as it slowed. The handful of passengers in Martin's car clustered around the door in their eagerness to exit, while he remained rooted to his seat. The burst of adrenaline that had propelled him onto the train was long gone, and now he felt hollow, sensing in his core that no good would come of this excursion.

The doors opened. He waited one beat, two, and pulled himself up. People on the platform streamed past the open doors. He moved forward.

Martin saw them the moment he stepped off the train.

The waitress stood above him, elbow jutting out from hip. Irritation had begun to dance on her brows. Feeling pressured, he blurted, "Just coffee please." He noted the flicker of annoyance on her face.

Martin didn't know her. He used to know every server in the Summit Diner by name. When he and Sarah were in their mid-20s, they'd come here nearly every weekend. It was part of their five-year plan to save for a down payment on a house. They called it "Saturday Night at the Summit" and congratulated themselves for spending $20 on dinner while their friends paid half that for a single cocktail at one of trendy restaurants in the city.

"Twenty years from now we'll be so glad we did this," they would say.

Now, almost 20 years later, Martin slumped in "their" booth, wondering just what in the hell was happening.

Losing his job was just part of this whole mess. He'd felt for some time that he and Sarah were drifting apart. They'd spent the first half of their marriage preparing for a family and the second half papering over the fact that one didn't materialize. They'd recalibrated--or, he thought they had-- by directing their energy into climbing the corporate ladder for him and ... well, he wasn't sure what for her. Until she quit he'd thought she was happy at the museum, and managing the house. Looking back now, he saw they were locked into a stultifying set of routines that just carried them from one week to the next, one year to the next. They never talked about anything. They just put one marital foot in front of the other, marching forward. And, now, apparently, she'd had enough.

He looked down. The coffee sat in front of him, cold. He took a $20 bill out of his wallet and placed it under the salt shaker, slid from the booth and headed back out, into the rain.

He sat in the Summit's parking lot lost in the imaginings of the impending confrontation. Which would be worse: acknowledgment or denial? There was no right answer. Finally, he swung the Civic onto the road and headed toward Ryland Acres.

The sky was a bruised purple with charcoal-colored thunderheads so towering Martin had to turn the headlights on even though it was barely 5 p.m. The rain was verging on torrential. The safe thing to do, he knew, would be to pull over, but he'd never cared less about being safe. Safe for whom? His family? Acid burned in his stomach.

And as he turned onto his street, he could feel it rise into his esophagus and his gut spasmed: the Volvo was in the driveway. He pulled alongside it and let the Civic idle a bit longer. The drumming of the rain on the roof was deafening. Finally, he couldn't stand it anymore and he threw open the driver's side door.

He entered the house and, out of long habit, immediately slipped off his wet shoes.

"Martin?" Sarah called from upstairs.

He stood in his socks, uncertain. She hadn't acknowledged his coming in the door in months ... years, maybe?

She rounded the corner of the upstairs landing and began down the stairs. She was in her navy bathrobe, her dark hair damp. She was loose-limbed, relaxed. He thought he could even see a smile playing at her lips.

"Where were you?" she said. "You're soaked."

Fury rose in him like a geyser. "Where was I?" he roared. "Where were you?!" Martin had never, ever, spoken to Sarah like that -- and it showed. Her eyes widened and she stopped on the step, the hint of a smile vanished. They stared at one another.

She broke the silence. "Martin," she said. "We need to talk."

As she spoke, he saw she was holding a manila envelope. Christ, was she divorcing him? He turned his back, couldn't look at her anymore. He was livid, but not at her. At himself. He hadn't intended to start out like this. He'd wanted to have a civilized conversation, hoping there would some reasonable explanation for what he'd seen. But her demeanor had completely thrown him. She seemed so ... so buoyant. Happy. As though she'd just been freed from something. Or someone.

The enormity of the realization nearly brought Martin to his knees. He'd lost her. He felt overcome, but not by disgust or rage -- by sorrow. A huge wave of sadness washed over him. For the monotony of their lives, for the two decades spent cultivating a career at a firm that would dispatch him in less than six months, for the family that never materialized.

And, now, for this. The failure of his marriage. He didn't even have Sarah anymore. The final insult. How had they gotten here? He could feel himself crumpling inside and as he did he felt a light touch on his shoulder. He flinched involuntarily underneath it.

"Martin," she said quietly in his ear. "What is it?"

He turned to face her. Her brown eyes, clouded with concern, searched his face for clues. He nearly choked trying to spit out the question. "Where did you go today?"

He could see her hold her breath. She looked down at the envelope.

"That's what I want to talk to you about." She inhaled deeply. "I've been wanting to tell you, but with the job situation ..." she trailed off. "I didn't want to put even more stress on you. On us."

"Who is it," he managed.

Confusion wrinkled her features. "Who is who?"

"Sarah, please," he said, stepping back from her and bringing a hand to his face. "Please. Don't lie to me. I can't take it if you do. Who is it? What's his name?"

The silence roared around them. Finally, she spoke. "His name?" she asked. "Well, I'm not sure."

"You're not sure?" Martin took his hand down and opened his eyes. He tried to focus on what she was holding up before him. Was it an X-ray? Was she sick?

"Dr. Straub called a few months ago," Sarah said. "He said the chances were slim but he still wanted to try it. I didn't want you to be thinking about this on top of everything else, so I just went on my own."

His brain struggled to process her words, and the photo in front of him. Finally he realized he was looking at an ultrasound image. An image of a small peanut, resting on its back illuminated in a shaft of radiological light.

He tore his eyes from it to look at her.

"Dr. Straub?" he repeated dumbly. A feeling of spectacular idiocy began to bloom in his mind. "You're not ... you're not having an affair?"

A look of bewilderment crossed her face.

"An affair? Martin, for God's sake ..."

"But I saw you!" he half-shouted, though with much less conviction now. He summoned from memory the couple in the taxi line. "You took the train to the city and met him and got into a taxi together. I followed you! You were wearing the scarf I got you for your birthday."

"You followed me?" Her brows knitted together briefly before she shook her head. "Oh, Martin," she sighed. "Dr. Straub isn't in the city anymore. He's up in Pleasantville," which, Martin knew, was in the opposite direction. "Besides, I'm sorry because I know it was expensive, but I never liked that scarf. I took it to a consignment shop last year. I knew you wouldn't notice."

She lowered the picture. "We haven't been very good about noticing the other one for a while, have we?" she said with a sad smile. "I don't know who you saw, love, but it wasn't me."

Now she turned her back to him, and her shoulders began to heave. Instinctively, Martin moved forward to comfort her ... only to realize she was laughing. Laughing! Suddenly, the tension in the air evaporated. It was just ... gone. As she turned back to him, the past few years seemed to disappear as well. Her face was soft, all the angsty lines and furrows that she'd developed--what he'd written off as encroaching middle age --were no more. Before him was the old Sarah: the one who would drag him to funky art shows in the city on the weekend, the one who loved to cook dinner for them and couldn't wait hear about his day over it. The Sarah from before the blood tests that had changed their lives.

"So," she said, eyes now shining with laughter and tears, and slipping her arms around his waist. "Back to your question. I think his name--and I'm pretty sure it's a he--might be Martin."

As he buried his head in her hair, Martin glanced out the still-open door. The rain, it appeared, had stopped.

Kris Faatz

HAZEL

When James Otis woke up on the couch in his apartment with a crick in his neck, the surface of his coffee table caught his eye. A collection of small Styrofoam cups, stacked in groups of four, stood next to a heavy pewter picture frame that someone had set facedown on the wood.

James knew at once who had done this. Only one person could have. He pushed himself up on the couch, feeling his age. What was he, now? Ninety? Ninety-one? Too old. He reached out and picked up one of the Styrofoam cups, feeling the beads of condensation on it. Much too old for that idiot J.T. to make a reappearance.

James carefully worked the plastic lid off the cup, knowing what he would see. J.T. had done this sort of thing before. James had lived here at the retirement community for the past ten years, but J.T. had only started his games in the last six months or so. J.T., the thief, the man James had been long ago, when his wife Cissy was alive.

Sure enough, the lid came off the cup to reveal a scoop of strawberry ice cream. James knew it had once been perfectly round, but now it was only a blob sitting in a puddle. He took the top cup off the second stack and opened it: chocolate in that one. He didn't have to check the third stack; it would be vanilla. J.T. was as systematic as he had always been.

James sighed and rubbed his damp hand on the knee of his khaki pants. His hips ached as he stood up, but he had to try to get rid of the burglar's loot. He had taken the first stack of cups into the bathroom and washed the ice cream down the sink when he heard the knock. Too late.

When he opened the door, he didn't recognize either of the aides standing in the hall. One was a young black man, tall and thin, wearing glasses. His nametag – white letters on a black background–said Gerald. The other was a girl with creamy skin and dark eyes and a nametag that read Kaylah. Something about her face made James catch his breath, but he couldn't think why.

"Mr. Otis," Gerald said, in a bright cheery voice with just a hint of scolding in it. "Were you down in the kitchen again, sir?"

James hated that voice. It sounded like a kindergarten teacher jollying charges. James wished he could draw himself up to his full height and look Gerald in the eye, but his back had been hunched for years. As peremptorily as he could, he said, "Do you think I was in the kitchen?"

Gerald folded his arms across his chest. His white uniform shirt looked offensively crisp and well-ironed. "Well, you see, sir, somebody took a bunch of ice cream cups out of the freezer. It was after lunch, when the kitchen staff were on break." Too late, James realized that Gerald had seen the coffee table. "Now, Mr. Otis." The scolding got more pronounced. "Is that any way to act, sir? If you want some ice cream, just say so."

I didn't want it. Even J.T. didn't want it. He took it because it was there. J.T. had always been a gifted thief. The best, Cissy used to say; you can get us anything we want.

"And now look," Gerald said. "It's all melting." He gave James a reproachful look. "You don't want to waste food, do you?"

Before James could protest, the young man came into the room. "Now, sir, I'm going to clean this up for you." He picked up James's trash can from the floor next to the couch and dumped the rest of the Styrofoam cups into it, in two quick motions. Then he pulled out the bag and twisted the top shut. "But you shouldn't keep doing this, Mr. Otis. Just tell us if you want a snack, all right?"

James tried to nod. The girl, Kaylah, had come inside too, and stood waiting by the door. James glanced at her and saw the smile in her eyes. Those eyes. Something about those eyes ... .

"Did this get knocked over?"

Gerald had noticed the picture frame that still lay facedown on the table. Cissy had picked that frame out. It was one of the few things James had bought her, actually bought with his own money, before he decided to let his other skills make a living for them both. *This looks like what rich people have,* James remembered her saying, looking up at him with her child-innocent blue eyes. *We'll be rich someday, won't we, J.T.?*

Gerald had picked up the frame to see the photo. "That's you and Mrs. Otis, isn't it?" How he knew that, when James certainly didn't look like the young fresh-faced man in the picture, and Cissy had never lived here at all, James didn't know. Unless, of course, Gerald had seen the photo before, been in this apartment before, and James had forgotten, the way he forgot so many things.

Gerald said, "Mrs. Otis sure was pretty, wasn't she?"

James reached out impatiently for the frame. "Thank you, young man." He set it on the table, upright the way it should be, facing the couch. Of course that would only last for a while, now that J.T. was back.

Gerald hefted the trash bag again. "You take care, Mr. Otis. And remember, any time you want a snack, you call down to the desk and they'll get you one."

The girl smiled at James again as she and Gerald left. Once they were gone, with the door shut securely behind them, James went back to the couch.

Mrs. Otis sure was pretty ... .

His eyes went to the old photo. James Terrence and Celia Otis on their wedding day in 1951, when the world had been different. When, for instance, that boy just now ... what was his name, now, the one with the nametag ... that boy would not have dared to talk so familiarly to any white man.

As if a gate had opened in his head, James remembered the rest. An August afternoon in Atlanta; heat shimmering up from the sidewalk. The doors of the church swinging open and the blast of heat as he walked outside with Cissy's arm through his. Her fingers gripping his wrist. The photographer scuttling ahead to take a photo of the newlyweds, and James already knowing what a mistake he had made. What he had, yes, thrown away.

Hazel.

No. J.T., damn him, was bringing that name back too. James had tried to bury it years ago.

She had been so pretty. James wondered, helplessly, how her face – that creamy skin, those striking dark eyes – could stand out so brightly in his fading memory. He could see her as clearly as he had that first time he'd stood talking to her at the drugstore soda fountain.

What if she had kept the truth to herself? What if she had married him, the way they'd planned when they were eighteen and the world seemed wide-open, and he had never known her secret?

James knew that J.T. would have turned the picture over again, right now. He'd have tried to erase the past, when a man had walked away from the woman he loved because she had told him something he hadn't wanted to hear.

I thought she was white. Anyone would have.

James sat still. Rings of condensation on the table showed where J.T.'s last loot had been. James didn't look at the photo, but he thought he could feel the sun beating down on him, and Cissy's fingers clutching his arm.

It was evening. J.T. found himself in a brightly lit room, across a dinner table from an old woman with pure silver hair and tissue-paper skin. She was talking to him eagerly, familiarly, with a smile that suggested they knew each other well. Her lavender jacket had the soft sheen of silk. J.T.'s eyes stopped on the brooch on her lapel.

It had a filigreed setting as silver as her hair. The stone in its center, smaller than a dime but bigger than a pea, glittered with deep blue fire.

Sapphire. J.T. had seen plenty of good imitations, when a skilled forger had cut glass carefully and polished it well, but you could never get exactly the right kind of light out of a fake stone. This woman's brooch had it. The setting could be sterling, but with a stone that quality, J.T. would bet on platinum. A ring of diamonds surrounded the sapphire, small enough stones, but probably not chips. Sapphires and diamonds went together like blueberries and cream ... . God, that was one of Cissy's lines. J.T. shook his head.

"I know," the woman said, as if he had answered something. "Can you believe it? *Triplet boys.*" Her voice, robust as a strong fruity wine, didn't quite match her delicate face. "I said to my granddaughter, 'Oh, honey,' I said, 'you know I want some great-grandbabies, but you didn't have to have them all at once!' "

She laughed. J.T. made himself laugh with her. Where was Cissy? She had set this up, no doubt, dangled herself as bait to lure this old woman in. Cissy with her child-blond, child-silky hair, and those wide blue eyes. And then she'd have brought J.T. over, introduced him to the old lady so he could get an eyeful of that brooch. Now she would want him to take care of it, baby.

J.T. wasn't sure what else he and the woman said to each other, or when Cissy came back to find him. She must have, because later he was in a room he recognized, and it was dark except for a line of light coming in under the door.

It was time to go. He had done this before, oh, plenty of times, even if this place confused him a little now, for reasons he didn't understand. He couldn't bring to mind any specific jobs he had done from this room, but he knew he had done them. There had been no trouble. J.T. never had trouble. He'd learned pickpocketing as a kid: You got skills when you were small and fast and your family didn't have much money, and shoplifting had come just as easily. Burglary was only one step farther.

His eyes fell on something that gleamed in the dark, picking up the faint light from under the door. A heavy pewter picture frame.

Anger exploded in J.T.'s stomach, so hot and sudden that he caught his breath and clamped a hand to his gut. He knew that picture frame, oh yes. He knew the picture too, and he didn't need light to see Cissy's face.

We'll be rich someday, won't we?

You can get us whatever we want ...

J.T.'s fingers tightened on his gut, digging in painfully. He glanced down at them and saw, to his surprise, that they were pale, thick-veined, curled on themselves. An old man's fingers.

Had he gotten old? How could he have? He and Cissy had only gotten married ... oh, a year ago. Maybe a little more.

Hazel said she had to tell him something. She hoped he would still love her.

No. No. He couldn't think of this now.

She was crying and he didn't understand. "We're going to get married, Hal," he said, "we're going to spend our whole lives together." *She whispered it then.* "Jim, if you're going to marry me, you have to know, I'm ... ."

The memory cut off. Blood beat in J.T.'s head as he reached out and picked up the pewter frame. For an instant he wanted to throw it against the wall, but that would wake Cissy up and they would fight. Instead he set the frame facedown on the table and made his way to the door in the dark.

When he opened it, bright yellow light outside made him wince. He went down the hallway, which somehow he knew, though he could have sworn he had never seen it before. Cissy must have cased this place for him. She did that at every house they picked out. She could do it easily, because no housewife ever turned away a woman like Cissy who came knocking and asked for directions, or "Could I trouble you for a glass of water?" or "May I please use your phone to call my husband?"

J.T. tried to think. The brooch gleamed in his mind. Once, he'd imagined a different life, an honest life, but he had thrown that away along with the only thing that mattered.

A white man couldn't marry a black woman, even if she could pass for white. It was against the law. He tried to believe that was why he told Hazel he wouldn't see her again, not because the idea of her body against his, her bare skin touching his, made him feel sick. Her blood was alien, though he had never known it. Spineless, he ran away from her pain as fast as he could.

J.T. didn't care what happened on this job tonight. If he failed, got caught, maybe it could all end: Cissy, her wants, and everything he had lost.

Somehow he knew exactly where to go. His footsteps made no noise on the hallway carpet.

"No, of course I don't want to press charges."

James sat on the couch in his apartment, looking back and forth between two people. A young black man stood by the couch with his arms folded across his chest. James had a feeling he'd seen him somewhere before. On the other side of the room, a silver-haired woman in beige slacks and a rose-colored sweater leaned on a walker. The morning light through the window caught her hair and made it glow.

She was saying, "I got it back and there's no harm done. I'm sure he was just confused." Her voice sounded rich and fruity.

The black man said, "Mrs. Ross, he broke into your apartment." James managed to take in his nametag, white lettering on a black background. Gerald. "Even if he hadn't taken anything, just breaking in is ... ."

James didn't understand until his eye fell on the picture frame on the coffee table. It was facedown. *J.T.*

James cleared his throat. "Would someone explain to me what's going on?"

Both faces turned to him. Gerald's, James saw, looked openly angry. "Mr. Otis," he said, "I already told you. You broke into Mrs. Ross's apartment last night. You took a piece of very valuable jewelry."

James closed his hands around his knees to keep them from shaking. His fingers were thick-veined, swollen-knuckled. He wondered when he had gotten so old. "Are you sure it was me?"

It had not, in fact, been him, but he couldn't explain that. Gerald snapped, "The brooch was here on your table this morning. Right there next to that picture frame."

The woman–Mrs. Ross–interrupted. "James, I'm sure you didn't mean any harm." Her eyes searched his face. "You didn't, did you?"

Gerald said, "Your door was locked, ma'am. He didn't just wander in by mistake."

Locks had never stopped J.T. He didn't need special tools: a hairpin or a plastic toothpick would do. Fighting against rising nausea, James said, "But you have it back ..." Memory handed him a name. "You have it back, Margaret?"

She nodded. "Yes, I do. Right here."

She reached into her slacks pocket and drew something out. Deep blue fire glittered in the sunlight.

James swallowed. He felt sure he had never seen that brooch before, but he knew why J.T. had wanted it. "I didn't mean to take it," he said. "I'm sorry."

"You see, Gerald?" she said. "I'm sure he won't do it again."

No, James wouldn't, but he hadn't done it in the first place. Gerald said, "This isn't the first time he's stolen things."

James felt very tired. What would they decide to do with him? Jail would be a laugh at his age. Ninety or ninety-one, posing for a mug shot. J.T. had never posed for one. He'd never been caught.

James stopped listening to Gerald. He couldn't make himself reach out for the picture frame on the table, or stand it upright again the way it should be. Suppose everything had been different. Suppose he hadn't married Cissy; that he'd stayed with the right girl, all those years ago.

No point imagining that. *Go ahead*, he thought to the other two people in the room. *Do whatever you want to me.*

J.T. paced the floor. Late afternoon sunlight slanted in through the window and hit the picture frame on the coffee table, dying it orange. J.T.'s knees hurt, but he couldn't stop pacing, couldn't sit down.

He wanted to go out, but when he opened the door, a tall young black man stood in the hall. "I'm sorry, Mr. Otis," the boy said. "You have to stay inside for now." J.T. didn't know who the boy was, or why he was there, but trying to push past him would only make noise and draw attention. You never did that.

J.T. couldn't find any other door out of this place. The living room led into a bedroom, the bedroom led into a bathroom, the bathroom was a dead end. And where was Cissy? She had another job for him, J.T. felt sure. He wanted to do it and get it over with. He glanced at the orange-gleaming picture frame again, standing up in the middle of the table. Funny, they had only been married a little while, a couple of years at most, but somehow it felt like decades. Forever.

Someone knocked on the door and opened it without waiting for an answer. Not Cissy. The black man came inside, and he had someone else with him. A woman.

J.T.'s breath caught in his chest. She wore a plain white short-sleeved shirt, and ... slacks? Black ones. She had never worn slacks before, or such plain colors. She had always loved skirts and dresses, patterns and flowers. And she had her hair tied back, when she used to wear it loose, so that its waves fell over her shoulders.

But her eyes. J.T. had never forgotten her eyes.

The man had said something. Now he walked out of the room, leaving the woman behind. As the door closed, J.T. understood he had been given another chance.

Somehow he crossed the room and got hold of her hands. "Hazel." When had he last said her name? "Hal. I'm so sorry."

Her skin was warm against his, alive and real, but something was wrong. She looked nervous. "Mr. Otis, I ... "

Mr. Otis, as if she was any colored woman talking to a strange white man. "Hal," he begged, "don't call me that. Call me Jim, like you used to."

She stared up at him and he wondered if she was trying to decide if she could trust him again. Then she said, "All right, Jim." Her voice sounded a little different than he remembered, but he could understand that. She was anxious, just as he was. "Tell you what," she said. "Let's sit down."

They sat side by side on the couch. When he put his arm around her, she didn't pull away.

"Tell me about you, Jim," she said. "What have you been doing since ... " She hesitated only for an instant. "Since the last time we saw each other?"

She was so gentle, to say it that way. He didn't want to have to tell her about Cissy, or worse, about the things he did. He wanted to sit here with her as if he had never lost her, but she had asked him for something.

He started talking. Telling about Cissy made him ache. He wished it wasn't true, but she was real, just like the work he'd chosen to do. When he said the words to Hazel, *I'm a burglar, I make my living robbing people*, he thought she would have to pull away.

She didn't. "Why'd you start doing that?" she asked.

"Because …"

It would be so easy to say, *Because Cissy wants things. Because she wants us to be rich. Because she likes what we do; she thinks it's fun.* But the truth was something else. Carefully, he said, "Because after I lost you, Hal, I didn't care."

That was it. If he had cared about life, about anything, he would never have let things turn out the way they did. Every job had given him another chance to run himself off a cliff, the way he wanted.

Now Hazel did pull away, but only to face him. She took both his hands in hers. "Jim," she said, "I want you to do something for me."

"Anything."

"I want you to stop stealing." She looked him in the eye. "I know you and your wife have to have something to live on, but you do, don't you? You have enough money."

J.T. tried to think. Was that really true? He had done this thing for so long that he didn't know how to do anything else … but how long had it really been? Time wavered around him.

"Will you promise me you won't do it anymore?" she said.

Maybe he could. He would try. "Yes, Hal," he said. "I promise."

For the first time, she smiled. He knew that smile. "Good," she said. "Thank you, Jim."

Her name wasn't Hazel. It was Kaylah.

James understood that she was an aide here at the retirement community, that she had been assigned to watch him, to make sure he didn't go breaking into anyone else's room. He understood that the aides would now watch him in shifts, around the clock.

He didn't know how he had put those pieces together. Her name, at least, was obvious, right there in white letters on the black nametag she wore. Other than that, he only knew for certain that she was sitting here with him on the couch, holding both of his hands.

"Miss Kaylah," he said, "I apologize for whatever I've been saying to you." He used her name deliberately, so she would know he was in his right mind. It was hard to talk when her eyes looked so much like the ones he remembered. "My mind wanders," he said. "I have a screw loose, anybody can tell you that."

What he meant was, *I'm sorry for whatever J.T. told you.* J.T., that bastard, God only knew what he might have said. Somehow, though, James couldn't feel any real anger.

She blinked. He thought he saw the glint of a tear on her cheek, but she smiled. "You told me a good thing, Mr. Otis."

"Did I?"

"You said you wouldn't steal anymore."

He – *J.T.* – had promised her that, had he? James wanted to warn her not to set too much store by it. J.T. could be up to his old tricks tomorrow, or for that matter, tonight. Instead he heard himself say, "I would like to keep that promise."

Maybe he could, James thought, letting his eyes rest on her face. The sunlight felt warm around them both.

Pamela Andrews

THE MIRROR

from "The Lyme Wars"

As she drove down the long driveway to the home where she and David lived, Francesca felt exhausted. After they got married, she and David had worked hard to save money to build this home on a spit of land called Water View, where the Nanticoke River, the Wicomico River, Fishing Bay and the Tangier Sound joined forces to dump into the Chesapeake Bay. They found the bay side of Delmarva to be magical; spectacular sunsets and ever-changing seas, sometimes with crashing waves or often, glassy calm waters. Just driving up to their home was always relaxing and uplifting as she observed the temper of the waterways beyond their house. Except this evening, her mood was dark.

It was a Saturday evening and she had spent the day teaching classes at the dance academy. She was disappointed to see David's car was not in the driveway.

The sun was setting over the Chesapeake Bay. The air was clear, but ominous storm clouds were gathering in the western sky. A magnificent sunset was in the making, so she left her purse and tote in her SUV and walked out on the neighbor's pier to watch the brilliant colors create drama in the sky. She sat down on the wooden bench at the end of the pier. At the urging of their neighbor, Francesca and David used the pier as if it were their own. It looked like nobody was home at her neighbor's house so she sat alone, taking in the splendor of the vivid reds and fuchsia mirrored in the glassy calm waters, occasionally glancing over her shoulder to see if David was driving up.

Down the shoreline to the south, jetties jutted out from bulkheads. The bulkheads stopped the waves from eroding the shore, and jetties captured sand to create sandy beaches. The shoreline to the north was undeveloped. Over many decades, trees from the woodland had fallen into the water, so decaying tree stumps made walking along the shore difficult.

Her grandfather had taught her how to take careful steps through these treacherous, shallow waters to find soft-shelled crabs hiding under the stumps. Francesca's ancestors had lived in this area for generations and knew about life on the Chesapeake Bay.

She was lost in thought as the sunset passed and darkness fell over the bay. There was just enough light from the driveway lamp to see her way back to her car. After gathering her things, she went in the house and tried to focus on getting something to eat.

Francesca moved as if she were in a trance. Her mind was racing over events both recent and from years ago, as she brooded over what had gone wrong with their marriage. She had once loved David with all her heart, but her recurring bouts with Lyme disease had made life an unrelenting struggle. He had lost all patience with her poor health. For the past year, he had abandoned being intimate with Francesca, and nothing she did seemed to change that. She became aware of signs that he was having an affair, which culminated last night when he didn't come home. There had been months of "meetings" that went much later than his office hours, and, on weekends, blocks of time unaccounted for. For the past several weeks Francesca had confronted him with questions about whether he was having an affair, which he followed with denials. Days of inquiries and investigation had concluded this afternoon, when the private eye called to give Francesca his report.

Last night David had taken their son, Jason, to the scout house and left him there with about a dozen friends and three counselors for a weekend camping trip. Francesca got a text from David that Jason and his friends were on their way to the campsite. David never arrived home after that. She knew he hadn't been in an accident because he responded to her texts with cryptic replies:

DAVID   **FRANCESCA**

Yesterday 6:23 p.m.
Just left Jason at the scout house.
Counselors were there.
Camping trip on schedule. All is A-OK.

Yesterday 6:30 p.m.

> Thanks for taking Jason. Just got home from work. I'm fixing dinner. One of your favorites. What time will you be home? Love you.

Yesterday 6:50 p.m.

I'll be late.

Yesterday 6:53 p.m.

> I'm fixing crab cakes for you. Can you give me your ETA so I can have dinner ready when you arrive?

Yesterday 7:20 p.m.

Don't know.

Yesterday 7:27 p.m.

> Are you ok? Where are you?

Yesterday 8:02 p.m.

Stop bothering me.

Her mind was racing with thoughts of the possibilities. Was he gone for good? It looked like all of his possessions were still in the house, so she was hoping he would come home tonight. Nausea washed over her as she considered that their marriage might be over.

Faint sounds of a truck coming up the drive sent vibrations of anger and dread throughout her body. The front door swung open and David walked through, glanced up, made eye contact, then brushed past her without saying a word.

As of this afternoon, after the private eye called, Francesca knew David's lover's name, and where she lived. But she had to say it:

"Where have you been?"

"Why do you want to know?"

"Because I'm your wife. You have been lying to me. I know you're having an affair. I know who she is, and I know where she lives."

"I'm home. That's all you need to know."

"Do you think you can just walk in and out of my life with no accounting for your actions?"

"This is my house, too. I can come when I want and leave when I want."

"Don't you have any concern for me? What about our vows to care for each other?"

"I'm so done with caring for you," he shouted, his voice hoarse with anger. "I'm exhausted by you being sick all the time. Every time I think you're well, you get sick again."

"Do you think I like getting sick just when I think I'm in remission? I've tried with every fiber of my being to be the best wife I know how. I've tried to be loving, and I've worked to help pay our bills. I've tried to be a good mother, and I've supported you in your career. What else could I have done? And you repay me by screwing around with another woman! How can you just walk in here without a word of apology? No 'I'm so sorry to have hurt you.' No concern for our marriage?"

"Well I haven't been well either," David retorted. "You're not the only one who has been struggling. I deserve to have some fun in life, and you're certainly no fun."

"Fun? Fun? I admit that life hasn't been fun for the past few years. It hasn't been fun for me either. Could we just sit down and talk so you can tell me what you're planning for our future? What about our son?"

"Jason is a good boy. I love him."

"What about me? I want us to go to counseling so we can get our marriage back. I want you to tell that woman that your affair is over!"

David clenched his jaw and said nothing. He bounded up the stairs, got two large suitcases from the attic and took them to the master bedroom. She followed him into the bedroom and watched in disbelief as he flung them open on the bed and grabbed clothes from the closet and dresser, jamming them into the cases.

Francesca took a picture frame from the bedroom wall. It was calligraphy of his favorite biblical quote, penned in royal blue on antique parchment. She had given it to David for their first wedding anniversary:

Love is patient, love is kind.
Love does not envy, it does not boast.
It is not proud. It does not dishonor others,
It does not seek its own way, it is not easily angered,
It keeps no record of wrongs.

Love does not delight in evil but rejoices with the truth.
It always protects, always trusts, always hopes, always perseveres.
Love never fails.

- 1 Corinthians 13: 4-8

She placed the framed verse on top of the largest suitcase.

David looked stricken, took the frame in his hands, briefly considered its meaning, then tossed it on the pillows of their bed. He slammed the suitcases closed and stomped out the front door. He threw the suitcases into his truck and drove away, leaving Francesca stunned and speechless. She stepped into the living room and sat in the first chair she came to. She was in such shock that she sat there with thoughts swimming in her brain, like goldfish swimming in a pool. They raced by but she couldn't catch them and she couldn't make sense of any of it.

Jason wouldn't be home from his camping trip until tomorrow so Francesca would be home alone, to deal with the realization that life, as she had known it, was over. Her husband had just walked out on her. She was struggling to get back her health, and now she had lost her marriage. Sitting there in the living room chair, she lost track of time. She finally realized she was utterly exhausted and should go to bed. Not wanting to sleep in the master bed, she went to the guest bedroom and wrapped herself in the antique comforter on the bed. She pushed off her shoes but stayed in her clothes.

She felt feverish. Her muscles ached and she had a dull headache. She was weeping tears of despair, but fell into a deep sleep, and the night wore on with one nightmare after another. Storms blew in from the western sky with winds screaming, waves crashing on the shore and against the bulkhead. The sound of a hard rain on the windows and roof woke her, mid-dream, as her chest heaved with sobs from some grotesque nightmare. Francesca sat up in bed, tried to calm herself, then stumbled to the bathroom. The dim nightlight in the bathroom was just bright enough for her to see the way. A pillow was still in her arms so she placed it against the sink's edge as she leaned down to splash handfuls of cold water on her face. She was still sobbing as she rose up to look at her face in the bathroom mirror, expecting to see it red, bloated and ugly. But she was not prepared for the horror looking back at her from the mirror. Her face was contorted into such a twisted vision of agony that she hardly recognized herself. Immediately over the reflection of her face, strangely illuminated, there appeared another face: the sneering, mocking reflection of evil. It appeared to be a vision of a demon, rejoicing in her distress, his peals of derisive laughter filling the small room with jarring intensity.

Francesca screamed, then ran down the hallway, flung open the front door and vanished into the storm. She slipped in the mud, her feet, arms, and legs were covered in wet sand and dirt. When she became aware of her surroundings, she was out on the neighbor's pier, curled up in a ball on the wooden bench, still sobbing and clutching the pillow to her chest. The driving rain and spray from the waves crashing against the pier soaked her clothes. Through howling winds, she became aware of another presence breathing right beside her, hot breath against her cheek. Gathering her courage, she opened her eyes to see what demons she now faced. And there he was. Barron, the neighbor's German shepherd dog. He had followed her out on the pier. Francesca reached out to hug the furry, friendly monster. He was also wet, but just the companion she needed to bring her back to a safer place.

After a long hug, Francesca walked Barron back to the neighbor's screened porch, where he sometimes spent the night. She held the door open for him and motioned that he should go inside, but Baron refused and walked away. Francesca turned toward her house, which was foreboding and black inside. She went over by the driveway lamp to her SUV. Barron came with her. Francesca opened the door to the back seat and climbed inside. So did Barron. She reached to the back to retrieve a towel and blanket she kept among the emergency supplies, used the towel to dry Barron's thick, wet coat, then wrapped herself in the blanket. Barron laid on the floor beside her and nuzzled her with his nose.

"Oh, Ralph, you're such a good doggie," Francesca sighed. Her heart was warmed by the memory of how Barron became 'Ralph' to them.

When Jason was only four years old, their neighbors had moved in next door with their puppy dog, Barron.

The first day they moved in, the puppy ran right over to Jason to play. Jason sat on the front steps, scooped the puppy into his arms and said to the dog, "What's your name?"

The puppy replied, "Ruff."

"Ralph ... he said his name is Ralph." Jason said, with delight.

"No, sweetie," Francesca told her son. "All dogs say 'ruff.' That's the way they talk."

"No Mommy, the doggie said his name is Ralph. Listen. What's your name?"

"Ruff," said the puppy.

"See, he said Ralph." And that's what Jason called him ever since.

So Francesca and Ralph cuddled in her SUV for the rest of the night, giving her time to consider the vision in the mirror that had frightened her to her core. Was it all part of her nightmare?

In the mirror, Francesca had seen the reflection of a sick, heartbroken, and angry woman. The demons she had seen were within her. What had happened to the confident, strong, determined beauty she used to be? That person was now a sick Lyme disease patient. She was the dancer who had failed to be strong enough to make it in the New York City Ballet, the woman who had just lost her marriage to the man she had loved. But most of all, she saw the reflection of a woman who had to fight her way through a broken medical system that denied the severity, often the very existence, of tick-borne diseases. Indeed, most mainstream medical doctors denied that Lyme disease was a problem, and they were willfully ignorant of how to diagnose and treat tick-borne diseases.

Francesca recalled the prophetic words of one of the few doctors who cared for Lyme disease patients and understood the battles of his patients, Dr. Kenneth Liegner: "In the fullness of time, the mainstream handling of chronic Lyme disease will be viewed as one of the most shameful episodes in the history of medicine, because elements of academic medicine, elements of the government, and virtually the entire insurance industry have colluded to deny a disease."

The reflection in the mirror was of all the defeats life had handed her. The feedback she got from others was part of the mirror through which she saw herself; the snub of friends, the breakup of her marriage, and illness that destroyed her dreams. She was a survivor who had researched information to help herself and others to be their own best advocates. Francesca needed to find that strong, determined woman again, she wanted to see the reflection of her successes. She was more than the sum of all her pain. She fell asleep with that positive thought on her mind.

Francesca woke up to the smell of damp dog, and realized that the sun was rising. She turned to Ralph and said, "We need to get you home before your people discover that you spent the night out gallivanting." She gave him an ear massage, then opened the car door so that Barron could go back home.

Francesca was to go to town this afternoon to get Jason, who would be coming home from his camping trip. She would have to come up with a way of telling him that his father had left them. That would be very upsetting for Jason to hear, and there was no good way to say it. She walked up to her front door and back into her home, ready for the battle to find herself and her life again. Through pain and illness, she needed to find wellness, and the woman she once was.

Carol Casey

WIDOW

Melanie Taylor left the yoga retreat mid-lotus, still wearing the loose white cotton meditation pajamas she had on when Sheriff LePrince's emergency call came to the yoga center. By the time she had rolled up her mat to leave, it seemed everyone in the session had intuited that something terrible had happened. Rising from their own lotuses, her fellow yoginis surrounded her, offering words of compassion that Melanie felt quite guilty accepting. They couldn't know that this latest event in her married life, although happening earlier than she'd expected, was not an unwelcome one. Cooing sympathy, the white-clothed cohort followed her to the car. As she pulled out of the lot, they put their hands together with one last "Namaste," sending her off into widowhood.

She began making her distracted way back home from the spa in West Virginia to Betterton. Despite exhortations by the smooth-taking Australian GPS guy, she missed several important turns. After yet another U-turn in yet another tiny hamlet, she cursed the car industry for dragging its feet on self-driving cars. If she had one, she wouldn't have to think about taking a left in 300 yards, would she? Who ever knew how far 300 yards was anyway?

Given her mercurial emotions, it was a wonder she could negotiate the trip home at all. For much of the ride in the otherwise silent Tesla Melanie shouted at absent Bob for cutting short her spa week ("Just once," she sniffed, "I would like to go for a spa week and actually get a spa week.") and at the same time putting her in yet another awkward position. Considerate husbands died in bed of heart attacks or succumbed in hospice after long debilitating illnesses. They passed in expected places, under accepted conditions, at convenient times, "peacefully," surrounded by their "loving family." Not Bob. Nooo. He had to land head first, or whatever, on a beach in a wildlife refuge.

Blowing her nose with one of those soft lotion-infused tissues she loved, she came back to herself. What the heck was Bob doing there?

WIDOW | *Carol Casey*

"Found by a woman," the sheriff had said.

She met her reddened eyes in the rearview mirror: he was meeting someone, probably a woman, (which woman?). And she knew in her heart this was the most likely story. Unbidden, her mind turned to poison ivy and chiggers. But Bob wouldn't suffer those indignities because he was dead. Melanie had never believed in hell but she saw the merit of the pagan underworld, that dark place of disembodied spirits. She believed Bob deserved to be someplace like that, wandering in a fog forever.

She sighed, anger and tears abated. Bob, finally a victim of his own evil appetites.

Then her anger was reignited by the thought of Bob, meeting yet another woman while she was out of town. Melanie began to wonder, was this one of the stages of grief she'd heard about?

No, definitely not, she answered herself, sitting up straighter and dabbing at her eyes with the tissue. This was righteous anger. She pulled the tissue away from her eyes suddenly. Was it dangerous to use lotion-soaked tissues on your eyes? Had they tested this on rabbits to see if it caused blindness? Wouldn't they have to put some sort of disclaimer on the box? And if she did go blind, there would be no Bob to help her negotiate her dark world.

"Ha!" she snorted as she balled up the tissue and tossed it on the passenger seat. "As if Bob would ever be there for me." Still, she was alive and Bob wasn't and she wasn't feeling as triumphant as she thought she would have, being the last one standing. She reconsidered her initial plan to walk into the morgue and slap Bob's cold dead face.

On the phone the sheriff said she had to come identify the body in the hospital morgue when she got back. How to prepare? Safe and comfortable though she felt in her yogic pajamas, entering a morgue in them and with her bare feet seemed creepy and highly unsanitary. Why hadn't Vogue published an article on what to wear to identify your husband's body? She turned her mind to fashion. Nothing too studied or too casual. Black was pushing it, as if she couldn't wait to get on with the funeral as soon as possible, which was true, but. The herringbone striped palazzos? Too joie de vivre. A simple gray A-line dress? Stagey and too formal, especially in Kent County. And definitely no platform sandals—like a merry widow returned from a tropical holiday. Ah! A simple white shirt and those jeans she loved—Rich and

Skinny, no holes, no tears—and navy clogs. Simple, comforting, down-to-earth clothes.

"Down to earth." Bob had taken that to an extreme. Then came a vision of an opened grave and Bob's flesh slowly deliquescing under the earth until nothing but a skeleton would be left of him. Skeletons. Something Bob had plenty of.

Cremation was definitely the way to go.

But before she could commence with all the details that go into disposing of the dead, she'd do what she had to do—verify that it was indeed her wayward husband lying in the morgue. After that, she'd be free until the inevitable formalities. She looked forward to driving back to the house after going to the morgue and pouring herself a cool glass of sauvignon blanc. She'd take it to the sunroom, the one room of the house she'd had complete freedom to decorate because Bob said he didn't like sunlight. Then, she and Heinrich, their schnauzer, would sit together on the black and red flowered love seat.

She started to notice the late summer Kent County landscape. Under a beautiful cloudless September day, the sun lit the brown soybeans and turned the corn stalks gold. A slight breeze ruffled them. Overhead geese honked, flying to their winter grounds. The wide two-lane road was empty and all around her the old was about to be harvested to make way for the new.

She would donate all the furniture but the sunroom's and then redo the whole house.

Musing somewhat happily at the thought of cleansing redecoration, she noticed the sign for Turners Creek Road on her right. At the end of that road lay the refuge where Bob's life also ended. She gave a little wave.

"Goodbye, Bob," she said, her vacillating mood on the upswing. "From now on, Heinrich is welcome on the furniture. And he and I will get a cat!"— the ultimate refutation of Bob's pet decrees.

As quickly as she was up, however, she was down. The fact of Bob being gone seemed beyond comprehension, but she couldn't shake the feeling of emptiness. Maybe that was why the sheriff wanted her to identify him: to make it real. Remembering that she'd left the house to go to the spa without even a wave goodbye, well, she could make up for that, too, when she saw him at the morgue.

She tried to imagine the scene. Bob would be cold, so she didn't want to touch him. Was that weird? He'd be grim-looking and, she hoped, under a sheet. She would walk in and nod her head like they did on TV so they could pull back the sheet, or maybe the sheet would already be pulled back? Would she cry? Would the sheriff wonder about her if she didn't? Would she be alone? Would she even miss Bob? Her eyes filled again with surprise tears. Even given the sad state of their marriage, she couldn't cheerily toss away all those years, could she?

She had no answer.

"Breathe," she said to bring herself back to the moment. Deep diaphragmatic breaths, in and out, remembering the soothing voice of Yogi Mishran. Ujjayi breaths. She came to the fork in the road, one leading to Rock Hall, the other, home. She recalled another Yogi's advice. "When you come to a fork in the road, take it." She took it.

Carol Casey

THIS IS NOT A DREAM ABOUT SEX

Into the concrete yard my dead Kevin came looking for his tool.
He knew that my lover had used it and thought he'd used it wrong.

This, Kevin said, picking up a gunmetal piston, is not to be used
to flatten or distress. It's best used to impress upon the plain and dull

something deeper. He pushed the tool onto a stainless sheet of
brushed flat metal. Each time he lifted his hand, he left behind

a hole, round and deep, edges filigreed, complex, unique.
Within the filigrees, darkness.

Sharon Sheppard

FIDELITY

wings collecting
what sun still bristles
into morning

summer's last honeybee
hovers
above the splayed rays

of a single dandelion
still craving
that sweetness

Sharon Sheppard

FAREWELL

Caught among clouds,
an old round moon
frays into night. Frost sugars
the blackened petals
of the roses. Along the horizon
a sudden stalk of lightning
flowers, then fades.
Every roadside puddle
lies lidded, and still. Why cry
for what cannot be kissed
or kept? As geese
etch delicate Vs
into November skies,
our world tips toward dark--
the diminishing bark
of their farewell,
another year's lesson
in letting go.

Sean Sun

THE LAST ROSE IN MY GARDEN

The summer is gone
All leaves are turning yellow and brown
A poor rose in my garden
Stands alone
Her sad eyes
Watching companions faded away
Desolately
She pines
To compose a song--
The Last Rose of the Summer
Before she withers so that the passing time
Won't completely forget her

Michelle Kreiner

BEACHED

Sperm whales share bone structure with the human hand.
–American Museum of Natural History

A baby whale is stuck in the sand.
Imagine this large creature
struggling to return to the living seas.
By the time I reach it, she is dead.
Waves crash against her body.
Her fluke beats on the beach,
    flips,
        beats again.

I am stuck, but not dead.
Time slowly ticks
as I wait for a protected path
back to the surviving world.
Heart and lifelines meet in supplication,
collapse to fists that beat on a door,
    flex,
        beat again.

Mary Pauer

BURN

I watched my grandfather burn to death. I stood by the side of the barn and watched him roll in a bed of leaves, the flames fueled by his jacket and his skin. I watched with a child's eyes open as big and wide as they would ever get.

The flames stood tall and grandfather lay low. A sooty smolder of leaves fallen from the apple tree and the odor of scorched flesh mingled with late afternoon heat. There is no other odor like burnt flesh. I would not smell it again until I was an adult and my cat jumped on a hot electric burner. I vomited on the way to the vet's office, and went into shock, but the cat was fine.

On that day though, Grandpa did not have nine lives, and he rolled slower and slower and then he did not stand again. I backed up against the clapboard barn and gazed with eyes which had not yet seen Fluffy's kittens born, which had not yet noticed my mom's pregnancy. I stood long enough. My eyes teared in the smoke.

I watched death before I understood anything of life.

I am told Grandpa, before his stroke, was a different man, a methodical and caring man, who, because I cried when he carried me as a baby, shaved his mustache. Then I loved him and never cried again.

This is not that memory.

This is my own story because no one has told me what that afternoon meant or why I was chosen to witness. It is not one of those stories so rich you want to savor its aroma with the Thanksgiving coffee and dessert of pumpkin pie. This is not one of those stories told over and over, because after one telling you are stuffed and it sits unsettled on overindulgence as does rich food.

This is a wizened story, events dried and long past, but not wiser with age. I tell this now to find the meaning I did not understand on that day and have not yet understood.

I was at the far corner of the chicken coop, where I wasn't supposed to be, in a spot where Grandma could not see me from the house. I teased the roosters because she told me not to and because I didn't like her as well as my other grandma, who liked me better too.

I poked the rooster with a stick just to annoy, to agitate, and deliberately to disobey the grandmother who always told me what to do. The rooster rushed me, angry with beady eyes, but with my weapon I was more powerful and made him back away. I did not want to hurt him, just to be the picador in his life.

This is what I tell myself in later and more mature years, although I think this is a lie, the kind you tell yourself because you are afraid if you tell the truth, no one will love you; you won't love yourself.

Grandma clucked and fussed and adored Grandpa with a fierceness I envied.

When she put me down for a nap, I scratched her headboard with my hair clip, just below the pillow line. I want to tell you I did that on the same day, to exculpate my spite, in hopes you might gasp and say, oh, poor thing; don't worry, no wonder; it was the grief you couldn't express.

I want it to be that day because Grandpa's bed was empty.

If it wasn't that day I hope to be excused as a child who did not understand, but that is not sufficient for the jealousy, the spite, the disobedience. If it wasn't that day, I have to admit bad intentions.

I hid underneath the porch that same day, or the day before. Grandma was always peering out the door, anxious to locate me. The fact that I was missing was the reason, I am certain, she looked into the back garden that late afternoon. On that day I switched my eyes from the flames to the house, perhaps to find my grandmother. I noticed her at last, peering through the glass storm door, watching her husband burn. Her open mouth, round and large and voiceless, hovered over her bib apron starched white against the darkness of her lips.

That afternoon I stood at the corner of the chicken coop and did not speak. I watched Grandma's face pressed on the door. I looked to the fire, and back, but Grandma was gone from the door. I did not know what she thought: perhaps I was responsible or, in the fire with Grandpa or, maybe she did not realize there was a body in the leafy pyre until it was too late for him. I knew only what a child could know.

The fire engine drove to the wide front of the barn. I liked the cocky fireman in rooster yellow helmets. I think one of them scooped me up but not before I saw the ambulance rushing across our garden, doors open wide, and the gurney with my grandfather pushed inside.

I think one of them scooped me up but not before I saw the somber ambulance rushing across our garden, doors open wide, and the gurney with my grandfather, charred ashes, buttons melted to bone.

Nancy Mitchell

FORENSICS

Ash slag tracks spit
glistened brick mud-boot

print screen door slashed
wall plaster cracked back

split lathing slats salt
frilled champagne

flute mildew ruffle
shower curtain hem

nicotine ceiling yellow
toothed #2 pencil red

wine rug spill blood
dishcloth scrub blot

Catherine Carter

WHIPPOORWILLS, SOULS

*It is vowed that the birds are psychopomps lying in wait for the souls of the dying,
and that they time their eerie cries in unison with the sufferer's struggling breath.*
–H. P. Lovecraft, "The Dunwich Horror"

*[Eastern Whip-poor-wills]' numbers declined by almost 3% per year between 1966
and 2015, resulting in a cumulative decline of 75% during that time ... In some
areas, parts of their range seem to have become unoccupied.*
-- https://www.allaboutbirds.org/guide/Eastern_Whip-poor-will/lifehistory

If their song presaged death, it wasn't ours,
at least not in those gone June evenings
when whippoorwills called from every dark field,
wood clearing, clothesline pole, while we still lived.
They're said to capture departing souls fast
in bristle-rimmed goatsucker beaks, maybe
to snap them down like sudden luna moths,
or maybe to guide them through short June nights
across the deceptively sleek-skinned boil
and swirl of river running like a vein
through understories of forever toward

wherever it is those souls are going.
Now when their twilit amphimacers
are falling quiet, following their razed
forests into memory, now I think
the loss they foretold and named may have been
their own. Or, given all those not-so-

endless nights of clear song, the prophecy
could have been for all the waning lives
which kept them alive too, stonefly, firefly,
ground beetle, weevil, measuringworm moth.

It could be so. But it's not like I know
what voice will lead them toward what lies beyond,
through blacker evening air than any sky
we knew. And when we can no longer hear
that call, vociferous invisible
guides vanished from the branches up ahead,
it's not like I know what might save us then
from being lost in trackless briar tangle—
not when any soul's journey is always
so perilous, not when there are already
so many ways to lose unheeding souls.

Nancy McCloy

WHEN THE MOON SLEEPS

And I growl, bare my teeth
at the night for being too dark,
too long, with demons flying
helter-skelter into sacred spaces,
creeping down numbers on
the bedside clock, screaming
their alarm at midnight, over
and over till

moonbeams shine
through my window, lullaby me
to sleep and the eyelid of day
slowly lifts

And redbuds grow hearts
from sticks
songbirds eat worms
sing cheer
lilacs channel
my mother's scent

And I walk down paths--
see strangers walk alone,
in pairs, or with dogs
while a kid shoots hoops.
All alone together; no one
seems lonely.

Catherine Carter

THINGS TO LOVE ABOUT THE RAIN

What it does in headlights: water-streaks plunging through the beam flash out that gold gleam like they've been waiting all their tiny lives, or their endless lives. Like water loves light, waits ready to praise it every second, every time. How the headlights seen through rain waver and glimmer, long lines of bright quivering. As if everyone could be warm and safe in the chilly gray.

How it softens the tough earth: if the dead want to come back, now is when. They wait for the rain to return, to speak in trickles, hisses, whispers.

Windows and windshields: lucid brief jewels tremble the windshield into clear oval waterlights, glass trickling past glass, the quick liquid sliding over the slow. The first spattered lines across a window, how they gather weight, round into droplets then drops, pulled again toward their path through earth.

How it doesn't have to come for weeks, years, ever. Grace you can't make, can't earn, can't force. Ignores guns, uniforms, laws, bribes, words. Say *please*: the rain won't hear. Won't hear if you say *thank you, thank you*, though you say it anyway because you can't not, because it bubbles through your tongue like seeps from the hill.

The shine it puts on the dry world. Harsh concrete cracked black asphalt sparkling and running with rain, roads for a little while turned back to shallow creek beds.

The voices it gives to gargoyles.

The domes and the bells, when children's umbrellas tip over into a faint, ribs up, to be filled with crystal cabochons and with flowers so small only the young see them, April's orchid tongues of henbit and deadnettle, veined petals of wild pansy.

How for those in need it may yet save everything, defer debts, feed kids, fill wells, raise streams, though often too much in deadly floods of mud, and usually too late.

The dapple-rings on the moving skin of river and creek, half-second-perfect circles intersecting the dozens of other half-second-perfect circles, not one seeking to be the only ring, each one crossing spreading rounding wider and thinner, all slipping down, downstream, away, now, now.

How it falls and falls on the mossy roof of the cabin on the mountainside deep in your mind, the place safe because no one knows where you are, despite there being no such cabin. How it gurgles in that roof's rusty gutters, sings in the downspouts, rings in the rain-chains, a woman humming alone in a house.

How it fills in your footprints, lets you be erased, washes you clean away.

Patricia Budd

BOLD COAST

Hike north until trees dwarf
from polar wind gusts.
Stand on cliffs at sea edge
where ledges rise rock-sharp
over surf and spray.

Here find nothing man-made,
nothing machine-crafted,
only wind-driven forms
that salt-mist, coastal silt,
and sand have allowed.

In the rubble at tide edge,
find shards; cola bottle,
headlight lens, poker-chip
chip, washed up detritus
of a world leagues and latitudes

away. Hold your hand, palm
facing out. For a moment
shun that far world, remember
this place, its simplicity
more entangled than we know.

Natalie Lobe

THE CURATIVE POWERS OF SALT WATER

Mix salt water with waves, tumble in the tide,
cool the concoction from deep fathoms below
where sea creatures live their lightless lives.

What comes into being is a giant cauldron
of balm, better than Gilead's, ready to cure
your weightless body of any aberration.

The rotating planet adds a lateral motion
only a snail can recognize. Seaweed exhales
a scent that galvanizes your soul.

Legends of the ocean and bay make clear
if you wallow in this brew you will be renewed,
guaranteed, money back, no questions asked.

Catherine Seeley

THE WATERMAN'S SON

My friend steps
Where Algonquins once trod,
Sluicing barefoot into the Choptank
Sauntering to an oyster bar's velvety mound
Just two hundred feet from his porch.
His Bermuda hems kiss the tide,
Cueing bare feet to read the riverbed
Like braille, toeing and loosening
The first salt water bivalves
Soon to become tonight's meal.
With manicured hands, dinner is scooped
Without tongs, dredge or culling board.

A flash of guilt zips through him,
Much like a quick glint
Of minnows in the know.
They've felt tremors of diesel engines
Cutting through deeper waters at three a.m.
Steered by sleep-deprived men and women
Working the water for sweet mollusks,
For palates which fast in months having no "r's,"
Then salivate in ones that do.
No bills go unpaid or
College dreams get deferred
If his catch of the day is small.

Two masts, a mutton leg mainsail
Made the only office

His waterman father knew
Where dress code was a jacket of strength,
Bibs of patience, suspenders of luck.
His skipjack's hard chine hull plowed
Through all weather with ever lighter loads.
The law of diminishing returns,
His hungry stowaway,
Devoured drive and funds
Stripping skipper down to steely resolve
That his boy's life will not repeat his own.

A son's eye can embed in the brain
Paternal images that hide
Till death stirs them:
The toss of the old man's cap
Inside the door, bald head gray-blue with cold;
His sweaty, bronze dome bouncing sun's rays
From aboard his Queen of the Bay;
The hunch of shoulders when a day
Of gut-busting dredging yielded not enough;
Salt water puddling his rims
As he reads his son's name
On the college diploma.

Returning home
With a net's bounty of fresh oysters,
The son wades and meditates.
A rising tide of gratitude lifts away
Any qualms about a life easier than his father's.
He knows hard work, a gift of father to son,
Is the jib directing his fortune's winds.
Skipper in his own right,
He's leaned into all seas
As deftly as he'd been taught.
Looking out at the westerly setting sun,
Silhouettes of old watermen seem to wave.

Ellen Krawczak

LABOR DAY: HOW A FAMILY OF TWO BECAME A FAMILY OF FOUR IN JUST NINE MONTHS

"Pay attention," I hissed. "This is really important." We were in a Lamaze class, learning how to breathe during childbirth. My husband was supposed to be my "coach," but apparently only one of us was taking this class seriously. I looked over to the desk where Bob was sitting, doodling, oblivious to the information being imparted by the nurse. He had drawn big, jagged fangs, teeth like a gigantic shark would have. "What is that?" I whispered.

"It's what a contraction looks like," he whispered back.

I could tell that getting Bob ready for the birth of our first baby was going to be a challenge. Where I was constantly researching what we needed for our baby, Bob was nonchalant about getting a crib and baby furniture. He felt that we had plenty of time to decide on what we wanted, and I would remind him that anything that we ordered would take several weeks to deliver. Finally, after much nagging, I got him to agree to spend an afternoon shopping at a baby store that would have a crib, a bureau, a changing table, etc., all the things I felt were necessary for the big day.

This was a mistake. While I industriously went from aisle to aisle with Consumer Reports in my hand, Bob wandered aimlessly around the store. He had spotted a three-foot teddy bear and lost all interest in everything else. "Isn't this cool?" he asked.

"A baby is not going to be able to play with that for at least four years. Could you please focus and help me make a crib selection?" I asked. It was useless. He followed me up and down the aisles, not looking or listening, and when my back was turned he went back to the bear. Eventually, I picked out the things that we needed, and he told me that he was "fine" with my selections.

A week later, I was preparing dinner in our apartment. I was trying a new recipe and did not notice that it was past 6:30, the usual time that Bob got home. Bob rushed in. "I'm so sorry that I'm late," he apologized. I nodded, scanning the recipe one more time. "I would have been home on time," he said, "but I stopped to pick up a hitchhiker."

That got my attention, and I turned and yelled, "You what?"

Calmly, he said, "I picked up a hitchhiker and I brought him home with me for dinner." And there, standing in my living room, was the big brown bear from the baby store. My husband had fallen for a bear. We named him Ralph Rabinowitz, and he became our constant companion–joining us at the dining room table, sitting with us on the apartment balcony, accompanying us to bed at night. We took photos of the three of us together, proudly pointing to our new addition, grinning widely, already in love with Ralph.

I continued to drag Bob to Lamaze classes and he continued to resist. The final class we took was in a gym. All the women in the class were almost nine months pregnant, and the gym was crowded with so many of us with our big bellies. We struggled as we lay down on the floor on pillows. We were instructed to close our eyes and visualize childbirth. We had already learned all the signs of labor and how the cervix would need to be fully dilated at 10 centimeters. Now was the time for gentle relaxation. I settled into the rhythm of the soft music, at one with all the bodies around me. "Look up," my husband nudged me, "look up at the basketball hoop." I opened my eyes and looked up. "That," he advised me, "is how much your cervix needs to dilate before the baby can come out."

I had a doctor's appointment on the following Wednesday. I told the doctor that I thought that I was having contractions. "Believe me, you will know it when you have contractions. What you are feeling are just little baby pains," he said dismissively. "That baby won't come until Saturday at the earliest." I drove home and, to distract myself, I refinished three little nesting tables, which were so streaky, we never used them again. The "non contractions" were getting worse so I called my husband and told him that I wanted to go to the hospital. We arrived at 2 p.m. and the baby was born at 6 p.m.

Ralph was waiting for us when we returned home with Jeff, our new baby boy. He welcomed our son and watched over him in his crib and then in his bed. And, that is how, in nine months we went from being a couple to being a family of four.

Postscript: Ralph was there to welcome Jeff's baby sister Jen; in fact Ralph resided in Jeff's room until Jeff left for college. It was a sad day when Ralph and I had to part. I still miss his kind brown eyes, his shaggy fur, and the comfort you get from hugging your bear, no matter how old you are, or how big the bear. Ralph will always be part of our family.

Tina Rayne Dayton

WHAT IT'S LIKE

This morning shopping, my daughter's fingers
circled the cart handle, pigtails

springing from her head
like twin tufts of grass, as she pointed

to the gold boxes, the mouse on the medicine,
and the monster on the label of juice, those

details appealing to her
as cherries floating in a sea of green.

Yesterday, at home we drew
a curling rainbow—well, I did that;

she made blue circle after circle, connected
and spiraling like a tunnel

reaching to the other
side of the world.

Hold me, she called
as the mailbox clanked,

dogs howled,
and her feet pounded their way into my arms.

The day before or maybe Sunday—couldn't say for sure,
but those hours

when the sun spilled golden light
over the flickering leaves, and the floorboards

undulated with shadows,
she leaned into my shoulder,

still small enough,
and those hours

contain everything, like a pail of rainwater,
overflowing,

yet
leaking all the while.

Tina Rayne Dayton

THE SHELL

Water foams on the shore,
draws back, and repeats,

and the wet shell I saw shining—
before I could capture its slick ridges of years

—the sea grabbed it and tumbled it again
into the frothy ocean.

My daughter laughed
with not caring; she found another

and another
and another,

but I am stuck on the one
that I lost.

These moments of decision:

the lab tech
piercing the ovum membrane,

my thigh pierced by needle
after needle, us

making the appointment,
but then choosing

to not do it again.

*

Fish evolved
from ancestral vertebrates,

plants spread their colonies,
claiming the earth.

We go back, and there is the first man
and woman, fumbling.

We go back, and there is the nebula's
gravity, beginning

to collapse everything
around a single particle—

shoving the universe into existence.

I don't know, I don't know.

But at the beach,
the tide, soaking and taking,

the shell was there,

now it is gone.

Meg Eden

SCRAPBOOKING

Between the pages of my first
year scrapbook, a piece
of my umbilical cord:

dried like a fruit skin, crusted
brown like a pressed flower.
On the end, a couple light

hairs: auburn and white-blonde,
the same kind I still feel buried
somewhere inside me.

My mother always said
I'd understand once I had my first
child, but now twenty-one years later,

she looks at the dried blood-thing
like a woman who's forgotten
her own daughter's name.

My mother peels back the scrapbook page—throws the cord
into the trash. Good riddance.

Sometimes when I was younger
and we argued, my mother would say,
I won a science scholarship

with Johnson and Johnson once.
She'd pull out her yearbook
where her Russian instructor wrote

that she could become anything
she wanted to. When I was younger,
I kept many things to remind me

of my worth: a fruit-by-the-foot wrapper
from a Saturday outing with my father, the silver
medal given to me in an ice skating class—

My mother, having been given just me,
made what was never made for her:
books for every year of my life.

Meg Eden

WHEN THE KITCHEN SINK LEAKED,

The first thing my mother thought to save
were the dolls: fairy-tale themed, all in matching

coffin-boxes. My mother unwrapped each one
from gold script FRANKLIN MINT tissue paper,

pulled out their dripping certificates. The boxes were wet
and collapsed at the touch, but the dolls inside were dry.

What did my mother see in them? Laid out on the hearth,
they looked like dead girls, their porcelain skin hard

and white, cheeks painted for a viewing: Pollyanna
with the prism in her hand; Alice, a stuffed rabbit

with red stains for eyes; Rebecca of Sunnybrook Farm
with her pink dress and parasol; the Little Goose Girl in green.

My mother grew up with and learned from these girls.
I grew up with Princess Jasmine, Mulan, and Pocahontas.

My mother believed in old world long-suffering and optimism.
I believed I could jump off a waterfall, go to war, save a country.

She must've told me all their stories once—it scares me
that I don't remember. She's saving them for me,

she says—when I move out and have my own daughters.
Looking at the dolls, I see our resemblance: same

pale whiteness, hair styled by someone else, slowly unraveling
into bedhead, eyes eternally open. I too will die someday.

Sharon Sheppard

PHOTO: LAKE OKOBOJI, 1956

Damp hair frayed as baling twine,
I stand astride the weathered dock
in pedal pushers, terry top.

Boyish face more-grimace-than-grin,
you hold up a sunfish, all flip and fin,
trembling your slender line.

We pailed that swimmer, his silvery scales,
carried him back to our dingy shack
and left him treading his shrunken lake,

thinking to keep what couldn't be kept:
the long pole's jerk, the bobber's dip,
the perfect day, the glittered fish.

Next morning, we flew from our narrow beds
only to find him shriveled and dead,
stuck to the linoleum where he had leapt.

Doug Lambdin

SUN AND DUST

At our old apartment on Main Street, I first noticed dust particles floating in the sunlight. They floated on the air, golden flecks moving at the speed of lava in a lava lamp, on a sunbeam shining through our living room window. I would gently wave my hand through the giant shard of golden light, disturbing the micro grains of sparkling sun, trying to see if I could grab a handful and hold them up to my face. But they vanished on my skin. Pure magic.

Our apartment was on the second floor, the top floor, of a late 1800s Victorian that my father and stepmother rented for $200 a month. I remember it smelling of morning sausage, the fennel and fat filling the air, perhaps transported across on the sun and dust, embedding into our plush green carpet and matching drapes.

Our living room was a long narrow room that ran parallel to two bedrooms. On one side wall was our high-backed floral sofa and armchair set, which was situated directly across from an oak-colored Kimball organ and Zenith television, complete with abstract aluminum foil bunting. The leftover space in the room could just fit two people standing shoulder to shoulder. We wanted more, but we didn't need more.

I recall one Friday afternoon in my preteen years in which my father and I were alone in the living room. We had eaten carry-out chicken chow mein, but instead of digesting in front of the TV, I began baiting him into a little roughhousing, a cub challenging the alpha male. I tried putting him in a half-nelson, but as he was six-two, and a good foot taller than I was, I could only lock my arm under his and reach halfway up his back. I leaned in, my nose pressed to his back, deeply inhaling Right Guard deodorant. He suddenly bent over, and my feet were completely off the ground. I then slid off to the side, snorting like a bull. Then with all my speed and strength, I wrapped my arms around his legs and pushed. Down we went, a single pillar, a toppled monument, his left arm absorbing the weight of us both.

"Stop, stop, stop, stop, stop!" my dad demanded, holding his left shoulder, squeezing it, searching the joint. He sat there, leaning against the corner of the sofa. His face was frozen, his eyes searching up and out as though he could see before him what his shoulder was feeling. Something was not right.

I stood up, my hands out to help, completely inert, like an artist's poseable mannequin. At first triumphant--I had conquered superman. But then fearful--I had hurt my father. The X-rays showed only a sprain, though he still needed a sling for a few days.

He hadn't taken it as seriously as I had. We were just roughhousing after all. There was nothing at stake, at least not for him. But something had changed. A line had been crossed. I thought my father was invincible, impervious. He wasn't. It was the last time we ever wrestled. It was the first time that there was no magic.

Caroline Kalfas

CHEFS WITHOUT A RECIPE BOX

My son Nick and his friend Chase fill up my kitchen at 9:45 p.m. on a Sunday. My bedtime is in 15 minutes, but they are exuberant over a mound of dough that has been resting in the bottom of a pink mixing bowl. My son shows me the unbaked circle that I admit has risen nicely.

"What do you smell?" he asks while waving his fingers over the bowl to funnel the aroma gently towards my face.

"I smell yeast," I say, with no need to bend closer to the dish because the smell is strong, distinct and pleasant. The late-night teen-aged chefs armed with rolling pins and cutting boards are creating homemade croissants.

"Where did you get the recipe?" I ask, wondering if Chase brought a cookbook that I can thumb through while the bread bakes.

"We found out how to make them on the internet," Nick says, nodding toward his phone on the nearby counter.

I leave the kitchen with Nick standing on one side of the island with his back to the sink and Chase facing him on the other side in front of our refrigerator. The oven, set to preheat, is against the wall at the end of the counter. Space is tight.

I go upstairs and flop on the bed. I want to wash my face, brush my teeth and put on my pajamas as I usually do at this time of night. But the kids don't have school tomorrow because of a religious holiday. They want to stay up and finish cooking. Although they are seniors in high school with valid driver's licenses, both are 17 years old and cannot drive after the state-mandated curfew of 11 p.m. set for minors. Therefore, I'm the designated "Uber Mom" to drive Chase home across town when they finish baking.

As I watch the clock, I hear a playlist of music ranging from the vintage sounds of Hall and Oates to the classical tune of Antonio Vivaldi's "Winter," which my son is learning to play in orchestra class, coming from downstairs. They also listen to a variety of catchy country hits including Zac Brown's

"Knee Deep," Toby Keith's "Drinks After Work," Blake Shelton's "Boys 'Round Here," and Darius Rucker's "Wagon Wheel." I should have the song order memorized by now because if teen chefs are cooking in my kitchen, they are playing this favorite lineup of music, too.

My son often invites friends over to cook. He has collaborated on recipes with kids from the neighborhood, his cross-country running buddies, fellow classmates, and acquaintances from Boy Scouts. Just about everyone who knows Nick well has been in my kitchen.

Some skip the prep work and come to eat the food. While Nick works with ingredients to make a homemade pizza crust and chops vegetables to put on his sought-after pie, these guests watch an Eagles football game on our almost defunct television. The set has annoying, squiggly, vertical lines spread across the flat screen. As Nick works his magic with pepperoni and mozzarella, these friends wander into the kitchen during commercials and ask questions, such as "Why doesn't your family have cable?" and "Is your mother ever going to buy a new TV? The screen has been messed up since we were in middle school."

Nick has told me that some newbies to the house become flabbergasted when they learn that he plans to cook from scratch. They look in our refrigerator and pantry and complain.

"They want to know why we don't have any food in the house," Nick says.

"We've got lots of food," I answer. "The refrigerator shelves are full of vegetables from local farm stands and our garden."

"No," he says. "They want pre-cooked food."

"You mean, they want you to cook before they get here?" I ask.

"Mom, they want pre-packaged food like chips, hot dogs, and ice cream."

The enjoyable kids to have in the house are the ones who like to cook as much as Nick does. They put on aprons and chef coats. They bring their own cheesecake pans and extra ingredients. Upstairs, I can hear their muffled voices and laughter blended with the music while they work. They enjoy creating a great hummus bar, with bowls of temptations they can add to the chickpeas. They cook steaks and red velvet cakes. Unfortunately, they like their own cooking, so leftovers are rare. I'm secretly disappointed when they forget to save me a plate.

But Nick is earning a widespread, high-marks reputation for his culinary skills. On vacation, he cooked midnight snacks for his Bible study group.

Recently, he judged a peach pie contest at the local 4-H fair. He cooked a large pan of pasta alfredo for his high school cross country kick-off dinner. He cooks more-than-decent meals on Scout trips. And he has accepted invitations to cook at other people's houses -- once for lessons on how to make homemade ravioli and a second opportunity to try his hand at preparing pork chops.

What puzzles me most about these young chefs is how they get their recipes. They scroll on-line until they find a video they can watch and follow. In many ways this method is ideal. They learn techniques presented first-hand by a master chef and see exactly how the dish is supposed to look at each stage of preparation.

But nothing is written down.

What happened to the joy of turning to a favorite cookbook with pages splattered in sauce and frosting? Where is the jammed-full recipe box overflowing with ingredients and instructions penned on individual index cards, with hints, variations, and comments scribbled in cursive and different colored inks? How will these modern chefs trade and share methods and formulas or keep a record of what they have made before and want to try again? Won't key recipes be lost because transposing ingredient lists and instructions from a video is too time consuming?

Nick keeps a small notebook in the kitchen drawer with cryptic notes scrawled in pencil about various dishes he has cooked and enjoyed. The volume is like a cheat sheet for cooking. As I scrutinize the pages, I feel like I'm reading a personal diary written in a foreign language. The titles are familiar, such as "Basic Alfredo Sauce," "Classic Steak," and "Garlic Shrimp and Noodles." But the pages are filled with pieces, parts, lists, arrows, and dashes that make no sense to anyone other than my son the chef who scribed the journal notations.

Nick and Chase call me downstairs where they each hold cookie sheets topped with flaky-brown homemade croissants.

"They kind of got a little too brown on the bottom," Nick says as he peels one of the fragrant croissants off a greasy sheet of tin foil and places the steaming bread on a coffee-cup saucer.

"Look at all the layers," Chase says.

"The croissants you get at the grocery store, or even the local bakery, don't have all of these layers," Nick adds.

I'm impressed with the perfection.

"Should I add anything?" I ask.

"Like what?" Nick asks.

"I don't know. Maybe butter," I say.

They both chime over each other that the recipe called for a great amount of butter already, but I can add more if I want. I skip any fixings and take a bite. The outside layers of the croissant are crisp and toasty, while the inside is fluffy and warm. As tonight's "Uber Mom," I get to share in their feast. Eating alongside the budding master chefs and listening to them critique the outcome of their hard work perks me up and makes me forget all about wanting to sleep.

The croissants taste good and satisfying. I eat a few more before grabbing my keys for us to take Chase home. The kids continue to discuss inside the car whether Chase's mom will like the croissants, too, and how the French are exceptionally skilled in bread-making.

Nick and I return home after midnight, and I head straight to bed. Clean-up can wait until morning when we will savor the scant leftover croissants at breakfast. I plan to relish each delectable bite because chances are my son will not remember where he found the recipe or have saved or written down the link.

The instructional video he and Chase used to make the croissants is buried in a file somewhere on the internet, which has more layers than the homemade pastries that came out of our oven. An on-line search for "croissant recipes" produces about 82,600,000 results in 0.80 seconds. That's way more than a lifetime of recipes to consider.

Searching for "croissants" in the back index of one of my popular cookbooks takes me 16 seconds, which is 20 times slower than the internet quest. But I yield seven hits including recipes for both chocolate and almond croissants as well as information about making and baking the dough and cutting and shaping the pastries—all in one book, on my shelf, in the cabinet over the stove, in my kitchen. The instructions are right at my fingertips and ready to download into a recipe box at any time.

Kristin W. Davis

EDGES

Chopping onions, I curl fingertips
away from the blade, turn the sauce
down so it won't boil over, meet

an evening breeze at the doorway.
Leaves hint yellow, a gust riffles
the pond, clear at its center,

but weed-choked and still
near shore—quiet edges perilous
as cliff ledges, you dare not

look down. My daughter drops in
from college to collect boots
and coats, her Grampy calls, tells

yesterday's story. Cool air seeps
through the screen as clouds unveil
the moon, its curtain pulled away.

Kristin W. Davis

COLLEGE VISITS

We were up north when freakish warmth stirred
the geese toward our winding mountain roads,
farms lumpy under their spread of snow,

barns balloon-red in slanted light,
toward glass-and-steel student centers,
giant touch screens with stats and facts.

My daughter shooed me from the check-in,
peered into dorm rooms. I quickened to blot
video-milked tears in darkened lecture halls.

Back home, the geese revel in their wild migration,
honk and holler over one another, flapping
in sloppy formation, a V with stragglers,

a lopsided M, at intervals like flights
on a schedule. Even at 2 a.m. I hear the exodus,
though all I can see from the window

are bare trees, black boughs on purple sky,
leaf buds waiting out the last frost.

Natalie Lobe

PACK UP THE PAST

Leave it in a forgettable place
like Abraham. You know what he left behind:
everything, even the two who begot him.
Do you hear the conflicting voices?
Don't leave what you know/go out on your own.
Listening to his calling, the patriarch did take off
for the unknown, east bound for Canaan
with seeds of a nation roiling in his groin.
You can and I can greet a virgin morning,
if we leave behind the curtains, the blanket,
the crack on the wall, most of all our beloveds,
living or not. Their invisible arms reach out,
challenge our will to move on.

Sarah McGregor

THE OFFER

On a sunny spring day in 1793, Arthur, the twenty-three-year old middle son of a noble but impoverished family, and an officer in the 18th Light Dragoons, proposed marriage to his sweetheart, Kitty.

He was refused. Lord Longford, Kitty's brother and guardian, pronounced Arthur's suit unacceptable. He was too young and low of rank, with neither money nor prospects.

Arthur was so devastated he threw away his violin, his books of poetry, and his fondness for petty gambling, tenaciously turning his attentions to his military career. But he vowed that his love for Kitty would never die, that his offer would stand.

Sadly, and despite its romantic beginnings, the marriage that took place thirteen years later was not a happy one. The couple who would become the first Duke and Duchess of Wellington lived apart for most of their marriage, occupying separate rooms in the house when they were together.

But what if ... they didn't? What if they found a way to overcome the obstacles of time, and distance, and the overwhelming pressures of success and fame?

This, dear readers, is that story.

Chapter One

Lisbon Portugal, September 1808

Major General Arthur Wyndham, Lord Taunton, stared absently at the letter in his hand. *Kitty.* A vision of honey-colored curls and laughing eyes flooded his mind, momentarily blocking out the heat and dust of the British military encampment. He ran his thumb over the red wax of her brother's seal. *Scio Confido,* the motto read—I know confidence well.

"Indeed," he muttered, folding the pages and tucking them into his breast pocket. "So, the game's afoot." Standing, he tugged down on his cuffs and strode from his quarters, a squat house of stucco with the tiled roof the locals favored. Jogging down the front steps, he squinted into the sun, not yet at its zenith.

"Morning, sir. Catching up on a bit of Shakespeare, are we?"

"West." Arthur returned a salute without breaking stride. By his reckoning, he had just under four hours before the ship carrying mail back to London weighed anchor—sufficient, if not ample time.

"*The game's afoot*," West continued, jogging to keep up. "King Henry the Fifth, isn't it?"

"Eh?" Arthur had barely noticed the boy's continued presence, only now registering his words. "Oh, yes. I suppose it is. Act Three, if memory serves."

Truth be told, he had no interest in frivolous discussion, including the recitation of Shakespeare's words. But West was a good lad, eager to learn and an endless font of cheerful enthusiasm. Arthur went to pains not to crush the traits.

"One of my favorites, sir. *Follow your spirit!* and all that," West quoted, his adolescent voice regrettably jumping an octave in the middle of his delivery.

Arthur grunted. Had he ever been so ... buoyant? Without thinking, he touched his breast pocket where the letter rested. Yes, in fact, he had. Even now, ten years later, he could envision sixteen-year-old Kitty as Catherine of Valois to his King Henry. Two infants in love with life, they'd staged the scene for Kitty's doting uncle. As if it were yesterday, Arthur could hear the musical tones of her giggling attempts at a French accent. He could still see the blush of her fair skin, smell the scent of her perfume blending with that of the old earl's rose garden that served as backdrop for their amateur performance.

He glanced again at West. The morning sun glinted off the red-gold peach fuzz emerging above the boy's upper lip. Life was sure to eat away his youthful exuberance—a stint in King George's military all but guaranteed it. But it wouldn't be by Arthur's hand. Not if he could help it, anyway.

"West," he said, coming to a halt. "Find Major Ponsonby. Ask him to meet me at my quarters, in say an hour."

"Yes, sir." With a brisk salute, the boy turned on his heel, jogging back toward the cluster of homes relegated to officers' quarters.

Arthur watched him go. "*Follow your spirit,*" he murmured, shaking his head.

A decade gone and Kitty's brother had summoned the nerve to resuscitate Arthur's offer for her hand. As if they played a game of chess that extended over time and latitude. A game in which the toplofty Lord Thomas Longwood deemed Arthur's newly bestowed titles of viscount and major general a prize worthy of eating crow.

Oh, Arthur would discuss the matter with his friend before putting ink to paper. He would listen to the case Ponsonby would surely make for refusal. But though he might agree to consider the options, to carefully weigh the pros and cons before crafting a reply, there could only be one answer. *The offer stands.* Ten years ago, he'd said the words to Kitty's brother and guardian. And ten years or ten minutes, it made no difference. He'd said the words, and he would stand by them.

Turning down one of the orderly rows of tents vying for the precious commodity of shade along a stand of pines, he squinted at the sky. If the mail shipped out as scheduled, the puffed-up Lord Longwood would receive Arthur's consent within the month. After all this time, the past arced into the present, snaking its way toward his future.

Follow your spirit. West's words echoed through his head and Arthur scoffed at the irony. They were words only a green lad had the luxury of believing—a lad with more hair than sense and more enthusiasm than experience. A smirk twitched at the corner of Arthur's lips. *Follow your spirit,* indeed.

Chapter Two

Just outside London, March 1809

Kitty pressed the damp cloth to her mouth. The incessant retching had long ago ceased bringing anything up, but she couldn't risk fouling yet another gown. Her head lolled against the back of the carriage seat, all attempts at sitting with proper decorum long since abandoned. As were two ruined gowns, four sets of drawers, and yards and yards of menstrual rags. Would this journey never end? She both longed for and dreaded its conclusion. The very thought elicited a groan, and more of her maid's fretful attentions.

"Shall I have them stop again, Miss?" Maude patted Kitty's arm, a flurry of nervous fingers.

"No," Kitty croaked. It was all she could manage. Her throat felt raw and dry, as if she'd swallowed shards of glass.

Maude pushed the curtain aside, gazing out at the drizzle. "Won't be long now, I'd venture."

What was supposed to be a weeklong trip to London, the rain had turned into almost double that. Rolling and lurching through endless miles of mire, Kitty's motion-sensitive stomach could now barely tolerate even clear broth.

Along with her typical aversion to carriage travel, her trip included a bout of hay fever so fierce she felt as if her head might explode. When she'd boarded a packet to cross the Irish Sea, she'd naively welcomed the respite from the close confines of the carriage only to discover that she also suffered from *mal de mer*. Halfway through the crossing, her courses began, and she found herself fantasizing a leap into the dark choppy waters. A tiny spark of residual pride and the intolerable prospect of dislodging her rags were the only things now preventing Kitty from rolling up in a ball on the carriage floor.

She cracked open an eye to see Maude still gawking out the window. Along the street, tightly packed buildings loomed over the snarl of city traffic as hunched-over pedestrians scurried through the rain. It was impossible to judge the sun's position. It could as well be dawn, as midday, or even dusk.

Maude glanced back at Kitty, unable to wholly conceal her excitement. "Sorry, Miss," she said. Lowering her eyes, she let the curtain fall back. "Never been anywhere so grand."

Grand indeed. Kitty closed her eyes. Soon they would reach their destination, and her worst fear—she would arrive at her wedding alive.

An hour later, Kitty surveyed the master suite of her brother Tom's London townhome. Georgianna, Tom's wife of almost a year, had obviously not yet set herself to this project. Gloomy, claret-colored curtains swathed the ceiling-high windows and the solid tester bed where Kitty lay, supposedly preparing herself for the ceremony.

How much better had she arrived wrapped in a shroud. She closed her eyes, envisioning her body lifted somberly from the carriage, an inconsolable Maude weeping at her side. Arthur would bow his head gravely, mourning the spirited young girl she had once been, but he would recover. And in his heart and mind, she would forever remain the carefree object of his youthful admiration.

Instead, here she was. Her heart still beat in her chest, and a prayer still moved across her lips even though hope of a miracle had long since died.

The possibility that Maude might succeed in erasing the ravages of this journey was the stuff of fairy tales. Heavens, the passage of ten years alone was enough to incite a lack of confidence. Kitty sighed. A mousy spinster of twenty-seven was nothing like a lively girl of seventeen and she'd said as much to Arthur in her letter. She'd known what her brother was about and had written Arthur assuring him she didn't hold him to his promise. But he'd written back insisting his feelings were unchanged. Gad, the man may very well live to regret his words.

With Maude's help, Kitty lurched her way to a chair, sinking back into the heavy upholstery as spots danced before her eyes. She tightened her grip on her handkerchief. It smelled sour, as no doubt did her clothing, her hair, and her *person*. When Maude held up a mirror for her, Kitty stared horrified. The black bombazine of her mourning gown drooped off her diminished frame. Hanks of hair had escaped her chignon and hung in stringy ribbons around her face. *In sickness and in health.* Gad, but this was pushing it.

She groaned again. She was already late for the wedding—*her* wedding—and she hadn't the nerve to put it off yet again. She'd already pushed it back a day and she knew Arthur's time was at a premium. He was a military man now, much in demand. It was bad enough she ... well, she refused to add a lack of punctuality to her list of faults. Maybe if she could imagine facing Arthur—silly, careless Arthur, her friend and girlhood sweetheart—maybe then she could laugh. Together they would laugh at how ridiculously hideous she was.

But that was not to be. Across the open bible Kitty would instead face Major General Arthur Wyndham, Lord Taunton, revered military hero and *a noted favorite of the ladies*, she'd read in one of the newssheets. Well, *Lord Taunton* was in for a shock. Could she even make it to the drawing room under her own power? Maude and John Coachman had all but carried her into the house.

"They're waiting, Miss." Maude's nervous whisper confirmed Kitty's grim thoughts. "John says Lord Taunton's brother will act as vicar. His wife's due to deliver soon and he needs to be on his way. A Major Ponsonby stands best man and, erm ... They're waiting."

"What if ...?" *I faint? Vomit?* Kitty shuddered.

"Miss," Maude whispered. Her gaze darted around the room as if at any moment Bow Street Runners might pounce from behind a curtain. "I've an idea. If—"

"Anything, Maude." Kitty closed her eyes. "It can't possibly make things worse."

Maude scurried to the trunk. She rifled through the contents, finally pulling out a roll of fabric from which she drew a bottle. "Whiskey," she whispered, pulling the cork.

"Miss Parkhurst." They both jumped at the footman's voice at the door. "The gentlemen await you in the drawing room."

"One moment." Kitty cleared her throat and eyed Maude. "What am I to do with that?" she whispered. "I can't even keep tea down."

"My da's a farmer, he is. A good drench of whiskey works a treat for horses with colic. Relaxes the gut, and the mind."

"I'll remember that next time I've a horse with—"

The footman knocked again. "Miss Parkhurst?"

"Used it on all my brothers and sisters and me." Maude raised the bottle invitingly. "As you say, what can it hurt?"

"I can't keep down clear broth," Kitty repeated.

"Plug your nose and take as big a belt as you can manage."

Maude pressed the bottle into her hand and Kitty turned her head away, the mere fumes triggering a gag. At this point though, Maude was right. Something was better than nothing. It was perhaps fortunate Maude didn't keep a pistol in her trunk. With a muttered curse, Kitty pinched her nose and gulped down four deep pulls. The alcohol seared a burning trail down her throat and into her empty belly. With a choked gasp, she clenched tearing eyes. A shudder convulsed its way up her spine.

"Dear ... God." The room spun as she pressed the handkerchief to her mouth, hard.

"All right then, Miss. Off we go."

Maude has a very firm grip. It was Kitty's only conscious thought as she was propelled from the room.

Chapter Three

"She's grown ugly, by Jove."

Ned's comment prodded Arthur out of his own open-mouthed shock. He elbowed his friend in the ribs. Just because Kitty had not perhaps *realized her potential*, didn't mean she deserved cruelty.

But, in truth, Ned was right. Enshrouded in a nondescript black gown, the pale, wraithlike creature that was to be his bride shuffled into the drawing room leaning heavily on the arm of her maid.

Schooling his features into a mask of civility, Arthur walked forward to greet the girl—*woman*—he hadn't seen in ten long years. "Kitty," he said, bowing low over her gloved hand. "Here we are at last, eh? I sincerely apologize for inconveniencing you so. I had meant to travel to you instead of the other way 'round." When she said nothing, her features obscured behind the netting of her hat, he went on. "I understand it was a difficult journey."

If her appearance was any indication, *difficult* was understating things. A wave of guilt heated Arthur's face. His life in the military was a succession of planning and adjusting. Altering course to accommodate the weather, his men, or supplies was second nature to him. When Parliament dragged their heels making a decision, he deemed it a simple solution to hold the nuptials here in London rather than traveling to Ireland as originally planned.

Simple for him maybe. The spring rains were notorious for slogging down the roads and a lady traveling by carriage presented a far different challenge than a man on horseback. If even half of what the coachman had related was true, Kitty had been through hell.

He was a thoughtless ass.

Arthur's gaze traveled over the wrinkled material of Kitty's dowdy, black mourning gown, reminded of her brother-in-law's death. She'd written him of that several weeks ago, *and* that she was changed, offering him an opportunity to renege. He'd assumed it to be one of those things ladies said. It had been ten years after all—of course she'd changed. They both had. Still, nothing had prepared him for ... this.

Ten years ago, Kitty had been straight and willowy with shining blonde curls and dark brown eyes that sparkled with vitality. Unlike this woman, *his* Kitty always appeared as if everything she saw amused and delighted her. Joy emanated from her like light from the sun.

He cleared his throat. "My condolences on the loss of Sir Benjamin. You've been staying with your sister, Maria, I understand."

Kitty nodded, murmuring something about the children. Despite the awkward silence, he could barely make out her words. What a cockup. Oblivious to Kitty's circumstances, he'd uprooted her from her family in mourning to take part in this slapdash service. No church, no wedding breakfast, no family nor friends. Even that mushroom Tom couldn't attend his own sister's wedding, blaming estate business for preventing him from making the journey.

Threading her arm through his, he led Kitty to where Ned in full dress uniform, and Arthur's brother Gerald in vicar's garb, waited to begin the ceremony. And she nearly crumpled to the floor.

What the deuce. "Kitty?" Arthur wrapped an arm around her, pulling her into his side. Jesus, could she weigh even six stone? "Are you ... unwell?" He realized the idiocy of the question as soon as it left his mouth. She was very obviously unwell.

Her maid started forward, then seemed to think better of it, returning to her place near the door, wringing her hands.

"I'm fine, erm, much improved actually." Kitty fluttered her fingers toward Gerald with what sounded like a ... snort? "Please, continue."

Hastily, Gerald flipped open his Bible. Ned, standing at his side, straightened his shoulders, eyes focused on a spot over Arthur's head.

"Dearly beloved." Gerald began the time-honored words, his voice seeming to bounce off the cheerless walls of the Longwood family townhome. If he read perhaps faster than the norm, no one commented.

With each passing minute, Kitty seemed to sag in Arthur's arms until he was all but propping her up. What on earth had compelled her to continue on in this state? Had Tom forced her? Holy Christ, this was not how it was supposed to be. Arthur had spent the better part of the last six months— maybe even the last ten years—imagining Kitty's joy at the realization of their long-ago dreams. Despite arguments to the contrary—both hers and Ned's—Arthur had envisioned that Kitty herself remained unchanged.

Yet that was not so. And it wasn't just her outward appearance. Arthur meant it when he'd told Ned he wasn't in love with her looks. Over the last ten years, he'd found pretty girls and bed partners by the dozens. Not one had inspired anything more than mild interest because none had been ... Kitty. Theirs was a connection deeper than mere skin, or so he'd thought. But, dare he say it? Think it, even? Looking at this frail shadow of a woman, he could hardly recognize the vivacious girl who'd once owned his heart. It was as if a spark had been snuffed out, as if the connection they'd shared so long ago was severed.

Gerald's pointed glare drew Arthur from his disloyal thoughts. Quickly, and rather vociferously, he repeated his vows. He was nothing if not a man of his word. He'd promised to love her all those years ago, and, by damn, that is just what he'd do. Or at least make a rousing good show of it.

She'd made it through, praise God! Kitty sank gratefully onto the settee. Not only had she remained standing throughout the entire ceremony, with assistance true, but she'd repeated all her vows. Maude's father was a miracle worker. The foggy bliss of mental numbness alone was worth the substantial loss of equilibrium. Kitty focused her gaze on her hands folded demurely in her lap. That her groom had to virtually hold her upright for the entire service was *unfortunate,* but it was a debt she would repay, tenfold. If it took her a lifetime, she'd become everything Arthur deserved in a wife.

"Kitty." She blinked at Arthur crouched in front of her. "I ... " Flicking a glance toward the others, he lowered his voice. "I'm afraid I must depart."

Kitty raised her eyebrows in what she hoped was an attentive manner. Maybe. She hadn't been able to feel her eyebrows, or her nose, since taking Maude's cure. She took in the handsome face of her new husband. *The Beau,* the papers called him, and with good reason. Such a shame he had to leave, but ... . Well, hopefully by soon, he meant now. She needed a warm bath, a clean gown, and approximately one hundred hours of sleep.

"In fact, the PM has called a rather urgent meeting. It's terribly rude, I know." When she continued to stare, widening her eyes in an effort to concentrate, Arthur's gaze flicked to Ned and Gerald. With a sudden shuffling of feet and clearing of throats, they called out hearty congratulations, collecting their coats and hats on their way out the door.

Arthur rose to sit next to her. "I am sorry, for everything. I didn't ... This was exceedingly poor planning on my part."

He speared long fingers through his hair. Musician's fingers, she thought. Long and gracefully formed, she remembered them deftly wielding the bow of a violin. It was hard to imagine them taking up the tools of war. His chestnut hair was cut short, for convenience, she'd read, but the style looked well on him. Everything did, really.

"Get some rest. I hope to return in time to dine together."

Kitty shifted her attention to Arthur's mouth, belatedly registering his words. *Return. Soon?* She'd been led to believe he had to depart, as in leave the country. Tom had told her that was the reason for the change in plans, why she had to rush. He'd insisted she would barely make London before Arthur had to return to Portugal. Good God, she sat here with filthy hair, no doubt reeking of sweat, and *vomit* when at any time over the last how many days, she could have stopped to … .

Her breath was coming faster, her mouth opening then closing as words came to her and as quickly vanished like steam over a teapot. Her brother was a self-serving, manipulative beast. If she'd any doubt before, she certainly had none now.

"I am sorry." Arthur waved Maude over as he pulled out his pocket watch. "I …" He cleared his throat. "Well, thank you. I will try to speed things along, but do rest, that is, if you, erm, need to."

Was he blushing? Kitty was quite certain *she* was white as a sheet.

Christopher T. George & Abel Nobel

FRAGMENT OF A FILM SCRIPT: STORM AND GARRISON, EDGAR ALLAN POE AND FRANCIS SCOTT KEY SCENE

"Our country may be likened to a new house. We lack many things, but we possess the most precious of all—liberty!" –James Monroe

FADE IN:

CREDITS OVER:

1. EXT. BALTIMORE, MARYLAND–A DOCKSIDE TAVERN. A RAIN IS BLOWING IN FROM THE CHESAPEAKE BAY. JANUARY 10, 1841

FRANCIS SCOTT KEY *is drinking red wine in a darkened corner while studying the testimony in a current case. He is 61 years old and thin.*

A short, slight man enters the tavern. The fellow has a familiar small black moustache and alert eyes. He fastidiously brushes rain from his shoulders. He is EDGAR ALLAN POE. *Age 32. Not the mournful character the world imagines—he has a keen sense of humor and often a sunny disposition, even if, as ever, he is short of money.*

POE (*exclaiming jocularly*)

O, how the elements caress me so!

How this world simply *loves* Edgar Allan Poe! (*Pauses*)

Barman, your best Amontillado, *s'il vous plait*, my good fellow.

Poe's attention is drawn to the quiet man in the corner:

POE

Frank! Is that you, my old friend Francis Scott Key?

KEY

Ah, Eddy, *mon ami*. I miss our chats about literature at the old Seven Stars Tavern. We spent many a memorable night there, didn't we, son? (*Despite their age disparity, the two writers have a wondrous, almost symbiotic relationship.*)

POE
(*obtaining a cask of finest Amontillado from the barman, he carries it over to Key's table.*)

Unfortunately, since Ginny and I settled in Philadelphia, we aren't able to get back to Baltimore as we'd like. I lecture tonight on "The Poetic Principle" in the Egyptian Room of Odd Fellows Hall up the street a piece. (*Laughing.*) Some will say Edgar Poe's a decidedly Odd Fellow, but in the Egyptian Room I should fit right in" (*He winks.* KEY *chuckles at his old friend's wit.*) Tickets 50 cents but I can get you in for free. It would be valuable for me to receive your tips for improvement.

KEY

Alas, I am duty-bound to prepare a case in the morning. Always a delight to spend time with you, Edgar, and to hear about your burgeoning writing career nonetheless.

POE

Ha! Enough about me. Baltimore should be forever grateful that your wondrous "Star-Spangled Banner" put the city on the map. It perfectly captures the city's fighting Irish spirit and the absolute "Heart" of the American nation—the same yearning to breathe free that we Americans felt at the time of the Revolution.

KEY *smiles and sighs languidly.*

I fear I am a one-hit wonder, Eddy.

POE (*Smiling at his friend, he takes another swig of the Amontillado.*)

We men with three names need to stick together! Francis Scott Key and

Edgar Allan Poe. Frank and Eddy Create for the Ages!

KEY

Very nice of you to say so, Eddy, but I'm hardly in your league as a literary figure!

POE (*exclaiming*)

Tell that to any Baltimorean, or *any* American for that matter! "The Star-Spangled Banner" is a great national song, an inspiring anthem. Incidentally, Frank, you know I like mysteries—?

KEY

Bien sur as the French would say!

POE (*excitedly, speaking rapidly in a whisper so no one can hear*)

What ever happened to that missing Fifteenth Star from The Star-Spangled Banner ... ?

KEY

A mystery indeed. Rumor has it that the star may have been given to the Marquis de Lafayette when he toured Baltimore in October 1824, ten years before the Revolutionary War hero passed away in Paris.

POE (*exclaiming*)

You know I paraded as a young militiaman for the great Frenchman while I was a student in Richmond. You know, although I was born in Boston, and brought up in Richmond by my foster father, I've been around a bit. I even fought for the Greeks against the Turks and paid my respects to the czar!

KEY

Aw, come on, Eddy. You're not still telling those tall stories are you?

POE (*annoyed to be called out*)

Oh, who says they're tall stories? Did you hear that I flew a flying machine from the Lazaretto Lighthouse out by the fort to the Phoenix Shot Tower just up the street from here? All scientifically proven, Frank. It happened, just

like my trips to aid the Greeks and to pay homage to the czar all happened.
O ye of little faith! O Say Can You See the Evidence Before Your Very Eyes,
my dear Francis Scott Key.
It's all true, Frank!

KEY yawns.

Go pull someone else's leg, Eddy. No doubt you'll find others who'll believe
your stories! *(He jocularly waves a hand.)* Now I really must get back to boning
up for this case in the morning. Good luck, my friend, with tonight's lecture
on "The Poetic Principle" in the Egyptian Room of Odd Fellows Hall. Yes
you are indeed an Odd Fellow but I bet you will be a mighty big hit with the
Belles of Baltimore!

*KEY again bends his eye to the pages of a weighty law book while POE shuffles off
to another area of the tavern.*

[End of Scene.]

Richard Zappa

KNOWING JOHN ADDISON

His name was John Addison.

But no one in the village called him that, or Mr. Addison, or John, or Jack, or by a nickname bestowed on him in his youth by a beloved Nana.

He was simply called "old man."

I'd met him shortly after I found lodging in the village of Wilton, where I'd settled in to write an article for the *Westminster Journal*.

I will never forget him.

He changed my life.

"What brings you to our village, Mr. Hill?" the innkeeper's wife asks me when I enter my name into the register.

"I'm on assignment to do some writing," I say. "I believe that your quaint village has an atmosphere conducive to my labour."

"So, you're a magazine writer," she says over her shoulder as she leads me up a staircase to my room on the second floor. The stout middle-aged woman with prematurely gray hair pushed back in a bun waddles through the corridor like a goose, with me, a bag in each hand, on her heels.

"Yes, for the *Westminster Journal*."

"Would you be writing about our village, if you don't mind my prying?"

"No, no—nothing as interesting as that. I'm writing a scientific piece on the medicinal benefits from eating raw fish."

The woman stops abruptly in her tracks and turns to say: "And who might be suggesting not placing their catch upon a stove to cook like civilized people?"

Suddenly feeling the need to defend myself, I say: "Experts in dietary medicine, mostly," now realizing that my scientific article will have little interest among *civilized* people.

"How long will you be staying?" she asks, proceeding without further stops to my room.

"A fortnight, perhaps a bit longer." Changing the subject, I ask: "Where will the cobblestone road from the village lead me if I'm inclined to take a walk?" Sifting through a hundred pages of notes from my interviews with experts and a review of their studies is the last thing on my mind.

"To the most beautiful countryside this part of the county of Yorkshire, if you don't mind a bit of the bragging."

"Good, then. I'll grab a bite and afterwards take a hike and enjoy the splendor."

We exchange warm smiles, and I sense from the encounter that I've made a friend.

A light lunch later, I'm out and about and ready to explore the village's suburbia. I'm not disappointed. Lushly green, the geography moves easily between woodlots and pastures—a cow or two often grazing by the fences— to small fields of root vegetables, principally potatoes and sugar beets. The pastoral setting on a clear, cool midsummer afternoon is perfect for the pleasant stroll I hope will relieve my pent-up claustrophobia and mania from the bustle of London Town.

About a mile into my journey I come upon a run-down cottage. There, I catch my first glimpse of the old man. He's holding a small shovel in a gloved hand and is turning the soil and pulling at weeds that encroach upon a variety of flowering plants organized by type and color. The rectangular bed of blooming plants in the front yard of his cottage is in stark contrast to the rest of his property: the rainbow-colored garden, an oasis among the patches of brown grass and parched red dirt that abut the dwelling like a rusty old horseshoe. The borders of his lot are discernible from a gap-toothed picket fence that intermittently encircles the cottage.

His threadbare flannel shirt and denim overalls hang on him like a half-filled sack of potatoes. A golden-brown straw hat with a wide circular brim provides ample cover from the sun. A gray and white colored contour feather is tucked inside a red polka-dot kerchief that's tied below the crown. Curly white locks stream out from beneath his headcover and so evenly match his beard that he presents himself as an entirely acceptable representation of old St. Nick.

I can't help but ponder the kind of life the elderly fellow has lived, which to the naked eye appears to have been one of solitude and unfulfilled needs. I relish the thought of learning more about this intriguing old coot. It's obvious from his worn-out appearance and that of his cottage, with its peeling paint and missing roof tiles, that he has been living alone for quite some time. Rather than interrupt his pursuits, I pass by, fully intending to inquire about him when I return to the village.

"So, you tell me he's called 'old man' by the villagers. Why?" I ask the innkeeper's wife.

"Because, when my husband and I moved to the village twenty years ago, that's what everyone called him," she answers matter-of-factly.

I press for more information. "So, what's his name and what do you know about him?"

"His name is John Addison," she says. "The spinster Worley sisters, who are in their late seventies, say that they only have recollections of him being an old man and they came here from the county of Manchester to teach in the school forty years ago. Mr. Sinclair, who managed the bank for many years, is in his eighties. He believes the old man is nearly a hundred years old."

"Does he circulate among the villagers?"

"In the twenty years I've been here, he comes into the village once a week to buy his food from the greengrocer and his paints and brushes at the general store. He speaks to no one even when people speak to him. Then, he makes his way back to his cottage outside the village and stays to himself."

"Has he no family? A companion, perhaps, with whom to share his life."

"None that I know of. There is, of course, the story that late in life he married a beautiful woman much younger than himself. I'm told she is the model in many of his paintings. But she made off one night with her lover, a handsome young artist the old man had befriended who'd taken up lodging with him and his wife."

"An artist," I say, my curiosity enkindled. "What can you say of his work?"

"The old man, as Mr. Sinclair remembers it, was quite the accomplished painter who took the train to Covington every month to consign his paintings and buy his canvases. But no one has a recollection of ever having seen a single painting of his. He still takes the train to Covington, though less often. It's what provides an income to support the meager life he lives."

I thank the innkeeper's wife for the information. My appetite whetted, I set out to learn more about the old man in the century that's passed since his birth.

Afoot again, I come to his cottage. As before, he's tending to his garden; this time removing plantings whose blossoms have dried out from too much sun and too little rain. I can't resist the urge to speak to him and walk to the gate.

"Hello, Mr. Addison, how are you today?" I say. "I couldn't help but notice how lovely a garden you have. Does it take up much of your time?"

By recognizing him by his surname, complimenting him on his garden, and ending with a question, I hope he'll feel obliged to engage me in conversation. He goes about his business instead—not even a pause in his labour to look up. I speculate that, at his ripe age, he could be hard of hearing. Bold action is needed. I open the gate and walk over to him, smiling broadly so that my trespass doesn't alarm him.

"Hello, Mr. Addison," I say again. "I'm a writer who's staying in the village for a while. I couldn't help but notice your beautiful garden and inquired about you in the village. I thought I'd introduce myself and have a chat with you, as I'm quite interested in doing a piece on this very quaint village of yours and understand that you've lived here for quite some time. Will you give me the pleasure of some conversation when it's convenient?"

I figure the ruse of writing about his village might induce him to speak to me and give me the opportunity to learn his life story. Slowly and cautiously, he rises from his knees. Once standing, his back is to me. A full foot shorter than I, my six-and-a-half-foot frame casts a shadow over his smallish, stocky build like a full-grown elm. I wait until he turns around; only then am I able to study his face.

His eyes are piercing, coral-blue marbles encased below a prominent brow that's a road map of wrinkles. His face is mostly an unkempt beard and bushy follicles of hair that serve as a single eyebrow. What skin is visible is as weathered as the shingles on the roof of his cottage. His teeth are stained yellow nubs filed down by a lifetime of gritting his teeth, perhaps aggravated by angst over his indigent circumstances, or by wrath over his wife's infidelity.

I extend my hand as a greeting. He declines the offer. Instead, he motions with his hand in the direction of the door of the cottage. I'm momentarily confused as to whether he's inviting me into his home or simply swatting at a bothersome insect. But he persists, and when he hobbles into his cottage, I instinctively follow.

We enter.

The interior of the cottage is the antithesis of the exterior. Clean and neat with snow-white walls that are adorned with the most colorful artwork I had ever seen—landscape scenes with rising and setting suns all aglow in vibrant shades of canary and lemony yellows, fiery reds and luminescent golds, still life paintings of roses, tulips, irises, oriental poppies, and black hollyhocks in decorative vases on window sills. The flowers are so lifelike you could almost smell their fragrance.

The room is comfortably furnished with two armchairs; the cushioned upholstery not nearly as worn or soiled as you'd expect from decades of use. Yet, one of the two is distinctly more frayed than the other, probably because routine places him in the same chair day after day.

With a wave of his hand, he signals for me to sit. I know to take the chair less sat upon. He pours from a kettle on his wood stove two cups of tea. We sit looking at each other, not uttering a word. Only the slurping of our tea breaks the silence. It is a most satisfying time for me. This iconic figure, whom the villagers only knew from folklore and the anecdotes of the Worley sisters and the banker, Sinclair, has shown me hospitality reserved for a relative or close friend. And, in doing so, he honors me with an unprecedented private viewing of his magnificent artwork. It brings a smile to my face that lasts until my cup is empty.

The old man reaches for his blackened corn cob pipe and a plug of tobacco from a lidded ceramic jar on a table just large enough to hold it and the pipe. The aroma of the blend is intoxicating. He studies me as I study him. Not wanting to violate the rule of silence I sense is a condition of my visit, I remain mute.

He remains seated when I get up to view his private art gallery. I take my time, feeling that a pipeful of tobacco will allow me sufficient time to closely study each painting. When I'm finished, I see my elderly acquaintance standing by the door, his way of telling me my visit has ended. I go to him, nodding my head as a sign of gratitude. He does likewise as a gesture of goodwill.

I proceed back to town, taking the last few steps just before the road curves to look over my shoulder and catch one last glimpse of him. Predictably, he is on his knees, hunched over, with the same small shovel in his hand turning the soil in his flower garden.

I sleep uneasily through the night, wondering if my visit with the old gent is a one-time affair or the prelude to my further study of his life. I'm driven by an irrepressible curiosity to learn his secrets, be they sweet or bitter, and to understand whether his cloistered life is by choice or by happenstance.

"Are you off for your morning walk, Mr. Hill?" the innkeeper's wife asks when I pass by her on my way out.

"Yes," I say. "And you're quite right to be proud of how lovely your countryside is."

"I suppose you saw the old man's garden. He's kept it for as long as the villagers can remember. None lovelier than his, if you're asking my opinion."

"A labour of love for him, I'm quite certain," I say as I venture out.

I return to his cottage around the same time as before, figuring he's a creature of habit and tends to his garden in the forenoon before the heat of an afternoon sun can hamper his efforts. But he is nowhere to be seen.

I tap gently on the door so as not to arouse him too abruptly. Receiving no response, I wonder if the old man is unwell. I peek into a window and see that the room where we enjoyed our visit is unoccupied. Not wanting to invade the old man's privacy by peering through a bedroom window, I turn to leave when he appears from behind the cottage carrying a wooden toolbox full of paint brushes and canisters of assorted paints. He catches me off guard. Abashedly crimson-faced, I fear he'll perceive me as intrusive and insolent. But his response is as measured as when we first met. He goes to the door and motions for me to follow.

We share tea in silence as before. I gawk in amazement at the paintings from where I sit. Then, he takes me by surprise and speaks for the very first time.

"John," he says. "You?"

"Terrence, Terrence Hill," I answer.

He must feel that further conversation is unnecessary because nothing further is said. After we finish our tea, he gets up and walks to the door. I know to follow. We exchange head nods and I leave.

I return to my room to work on my article and am soon distracted by reflections on the events of the past two days. After only two visits to the old man's home and just a few words spoken, I've learned much about John

Addison—a quiet man, quite content to live alone, a talented artist, happy to fill his days producing fine artwork and taking care of his garden. He's hardly the broken-down, broken-hearted old recluse the villagers perceive him to be. I'm convinced the villagers are confusing his self-imposed segregation as contempt for them. But his cordiality toward me, a total stranger, proves that he harbors no ill will toward them, or anyone.

For my friend, living alone does not mean that he is lonely.

I return to the cottage the next day in the hope of learning more about my friend, John Addison. This time, I come armed with some tea, a pouch of pipe tobacco, and a copy of my book *The Very Peculiar Customs of Aboriginals and Pygmies*, which I authored two years earlier. The old man is snipping off an assortment of lilacs and irises from his garden when I arrive—blooms I'm certain will end up in vases memorialized in paintings that one day will hang on the walls of art shops in Covington.

He stops what he's doing when he sees me. He gestures for me to follow him around the cottage; my gifts, hidden away in my backpack for delivery to him when the time is right. My companion leads me to a detached studio that sits at the rear of his property. The room is quite large, about half the size of the cottage. Unfinished paintings rest on several easels. Benches and tables are strategically placed. One table collects an assortment of vases, ewers and baskets—the props for his still life paintings. A washbasin hangs beneath a large window with an easterly exposure. Water is available in jugs to wash brushes and the hands that use them. An array of unframed paintings adorns the walls; canvases that, once framed, will one day be a source of income.

A locked sliding wooden door separates his work area from a private room that contains framed artwork, which I see for the first time when my friend unlocks it and, looking over his shoulder, nods for me to enter.

I'm overwhelmed.

A dozen paintings hang on the walls—of various sizes with backgrounds of the countryside, a café, the living room of the cottage, and a mirrored bedroom wall showing the reflection of a bed. A common thread woven through the assemblage of art is the presence of a beautiful young woman. Her long wavy black hair is pushed to the side in some paintings, lying over her shoulders in others and, in one majestic pose, braided atop her head like a crown. Her hazel-green eyes sparkle and follow you no matter where you stand to look at her. A cream-colored complexion so pure in appearance, it is an understatement to describe it as angelic. When a full view of the young woman is depicted in paint lying nude on a bed, she is slim but with breasts ample enough to arouse even the most pious clergyman.

I know from my conversation with the innkeeper's wife the identity of the strikingly attractive young woman, and I understand the old man's reason for sharing her with me. It's his way of telling me that he once loved a woman so deeply that he felt the need to preserve her for all of time in his paintings—paintings he stashes away in a back room of his private studio, as a pirate might hide his treasure in a sunken cave on an uncharted island.

He moves from painting to painting. I follow a few paces behind, studying the myriad poses in which he has placed her; the detail of the facial expressions he's painted leave no doubt about her disposition and mood—be it gay, sullen, meditative or, as she posed nude in bed, provocatively solicitous. I'm so aroused by the sensuality of his young wife, companion and lover that I'm embarrassed by my salacious thoughts—thoughts I will relive in afternoon reveries and in late evening reflections that will make futile my attempts at sleep.

The last portrait viewed, I see him move to the door. I obey his tacit command and follow him out. We end up in our designated chairs in the cottage with a cup of tea in hand. I open my backpack. Taking my time, I convey my gifts to him, one after the other, as if they were gold, frankincense, and myrrh. An ever-so-subtle nod of his head follows the receipt of each gift. He honors me by placing some of the tea leaves in a new kettle of water and plugs his pipe with a pinch of the tobacco I brought him.

Between sipping his tea and puffing his pipe, he reaches inside the pocket of his shirt to remove his spectacles and wires them behind his ears. He studies the cover of the book I gave him. He goes straightaway to the end of the book to read my biography. My friend will now learn all there is to know about me. He looks at me and smiles when he's finished. I think how pleasantly peculiar it is that we find spoken words unnecessary.

Our second cups of tea now empty, my host gets up and walks to the door. This time, he extends his hand to me as I approach. I take it; his handshake is as firm as my resolve to nurture our friendship. For some reason I can't explain, I feel the need to hug the grizzled old geezer. He returns the embrace, though with less force than I, but with enough conviction to underscore his sincerity.

The strangest feeling comes over me as I walk back to the village. It begins when I reach the curve in the road and turn my head. My friend is standing over his garden with a Bible in his hands and reading from it. I turn my head back so as not to invade the solemnity of his private moments. But I feel oddly out of sorts the remainder of the day.

The next morning, I begin my day with the same feeling of apprehension that had ended the one before it. I soon realize my dread is warranted.

"Mr. Hill, did you hear about Mr. Addison?" the innkeeper's wife says when she sees me, an ominous tone in her voice.

"No. I was planning on paying him a visit this morning," I reply.

"The poor man was found dead within the hour. He was lying beside his lovely garden with a Bible in his hands."

I'm aghast. The odd way I'd felt when I last saw him was indeed a premonition. By his actions at his garden yesterday, he must have sensed that the end was close. He must have heard the creaking of death's door—saw it opening and the hand of God motioning for him to enter.

His prayers by the garden, what were they about? I wonder, was he praying for God's forgiveness for the soul of the unfaithful young beauty who'd been wife to him and mistress to his protégé? Or, was the old man praying for his own salvation. But, why would the simple good life he led threaten a heavenly repose?

The old man is buried two days later in the village cemetery. There is no funeral, but I arrange for the vicar of the village chapel to perform a graveside service. I also purchase a headstone and have the name of my friend engraved on it with the date of his death and the words, "He led a full and productive life." The mourners include the Worley sisters, Mr. Sinclair, the innkeeper and his wife, and me.

A week passes before my presence is requested by the village solicitor.

"Mr. Hill, are you kin to John Addison?" he asks.

"No," I reply, "but we were close friends at the time of his passing."

"That explains it then."

"Explains what?"

"When he was found dead by his garden, the old man was holding a Bible. In it was a note—a handwritten last will and testament of that day's date."

The solicitor opens a folded piece of paper and reads to me what is written: "All I have to Terence Hill, author, companion and friend. He will know what to do. John Addison."

The inventory the solicitor provides me describes John Addison's estate as consisting of his cottage, his artwork, and his personal possessions.

I lay in my bed weeping as though I'd lost a father, a brother, or the dearest of friends. I plan to take up residence at the cottage, and in a manner that will leave the old man's presence undisturbed. I feel an obligation to tend to his garden. I pledge to create another rectangular bed beside it with flowers I hope one day will be as striking and vibrant as those my friend had planted and attended to for so many years of a mostly solitary life.

My return to the cottage is bittersweet. I spend the morning drinking tea and studying the paintings that hang on the walls of his sanctuary. Like the pull of metal to a magnet, I can resist no longer and retreat to the studio. With the respect one shows entering a cathedral, I proceed to the back room, my head slightly bowed like a repentant monk on his way to vespers.

I center a bench and sit.

For more than an hour, I study the face of the young beauty in each of the paintings to sense her mood. I dissect her countenance as if I'm decoding an encrypted message. I want to feel what my friend felt when he looked into her eyes, her heart, and her soul. I find myself smiling when she smiles. I become reflective when she appears meditative. I feel glum when she looks morose. I covet her as she poses seductively in her bed. I leave the room feeling as though I'd seen her through the eyes of my friend, John Addison.

I return to the garden with shovel in hand. I begin to dig out the site of my garden adjacent to his and am troubled to see when I dig to a depth of not more than a foot what appear to be skeletal bones. I'm confused as to the source of the remains—a canine friend, perhaps, who'd served as a faithful companion. Digging deeper leads me to physical objects that I cannot readily explain by my deduction that what's buried had once been a devoted pet.

Coins.

A watch.

I take the objects into the cottage and clean them the best I can. The coins are dated many years ago. On the watch are inscribed the initials E.T.

I stop what I'm doing and head back to the village to visit with the Worley sisters. I make polite conversation with them about my reasons for coming to their village and how quaint and enchanting it is. I explain how John Addison befriended me, left me his estate, and that I planned to maintain his cottage and garden in good order. After gaining their favor, I ask them about the tragedy that befell the old man when his young wife abandoned him for a lover.

"This man, whom the young woman made off with, what might be his name?"

One sister looks pensive and indecisive, but the other is quick to respond. "His name is Ned Townsend. An aspiring young artist he was, who the old man took in as a son, only to be cuckolded."

I feel that the mystery, or at least a part of it, has been solved. For "Ned" is a common nickname for Edmond. I thank the sisters for their time and leave.

I walk back to the cottage in a stupor. Finding a long-handled shovel, I dig into the old man's garden. I go straight to the center of the bed where the roses are arranged in the shape of a heart. I dig deep, a foot and a half or more, until I find the skeletal remains of two hands. I do a curettage of the dirt around the boney relics, as if I were on an archeological dig. There, I find on the finger of one of the hands a ring, which I gently remove with as little disturbance of the fragments of bone as possible.

I return to the cottage and clean the object the best I can. I clean it well enough to see on the inside of the ring the words "For wife from John."

I sit in the old man's chair, but do not feel that I'm violating his private space. I want to understand him and, through this symbolic act, hope that it might help bring clarity to my understanding who John Addison truly was, not who he appeared to be. Hours of meditation while perched in his chair lead me to conclude that John Addison was no more or less moral, and no more or less righteous, than most any other man. The reasons for his actions I cannot know with certainty. Rage? Revenge? Justice? Insanity? Maybe a little of each. Maybe for none of those reasons.

Of this I'm certain, as I stand beside my dead friend's garden—John Addison did what he did because he knew it was the only way he could continue to be with the only woman he'd ever loved. He was with her in the back room of his studio, feeling her moods in the faces he'd painted. He was with her when he tended the garden that became a blanket upon her bed. He expressed his ongoing love for her by carefully arranging the flowers, being sure that only roses were clustered above her hands that were folded upon her heart.

I return the objects I'd taken to where they'd been unearthed.
I gently place the ring on the finger from which it had been removed.
I restore the garden and the ground to what had been before.
I hold his Bible in my hands.
I pray for the souls of those who lie beneath the soil.
I pray for the soul of the man who'd placed them there.
I return to his cottage.
I sit in his chair.
I feel I have learned all I need to know.

THE END

Jamie Brown

LABYRINTH

I find as I age that I dream often about the old brick scriptorium with its high glass windows, and especially the library itself, of which it was a part, and the rest of the monastery complex, and its chapel, its cloistered walkways, the labyrinth, the monk's cells, the refectory and kitchen. The scriptorium is empty now, but it wasn't always thus. Once there were six busy lines of copy-tables from one end to nearly the other. There had been some sixteen rows of copy desks, each with its circular socket for the inkwell which prevented the bottle of ink from tipping over and ruining all of the copyist's labor. At the rear were four large map-copying tables, arranged in a square. This arrangement had no significance in itself, but was to provide the map-copyists room to move around their work. Each sheet of vellum, whether for manuscript or map, was held down at the edges by sachets of sand to prevent it curling up as the scribe worked. Monks, inkwells, desks, and vellum are all gone, dissipated like the morning mist, or evaporated like the dreams themselves, gone into nothing but the tenuous memories I still cherish. The bags of sand are gone, too.

Sometimes the mist is miasma, full of sickly vapors that rise from the swampy remains of the cities and town in the valley below on those humid mornings that portend insufferable summer-like temperatures and humidity. Sweat runs down the skin and lacquers the body in a congealed patina of slime. It didn't used to be that way. There used to be sanitation, with water running through the pipes from the well, lifted and distributed by the monastery's low-tech windmill, and cleanliness, some said, was next to Godliness, although the original anchorites in the Nubian desert believed bathing to be an affectation of the wealthy classes, and therefore a matter of personal pride to be shunned by true disciples. Thankfully, we were encouraged, as young acolytes, to bathe once a week.

Gone, now, all gone, the manuscripts burnt by the raiders, the library destroyed, and with it, what knowledge we could have used to rebuild the world. Scriptorium, monastery, chapel, cloisters . . . all gone, not one brick left atop another. The darkness of ignorance has descended upon the face of the earth. We should have seen it coming; many did see it coming, but their voices were too few, and the rest of us too complacent. And even the labyrinth is now a choked thicket of scrub through which it would be impossible to find one's way even if one could locate the place. I fear it will only get worse before it gets better.

Joan Drescher Cooper

CELIA'S AUDIENCE WITH THE MADMAN

"Dr. Tregoning?" Nothing answered but the hum of generators thrumming in the background. Despite the deep, velvet black, Celia sensed there was something else in the room with her. Then a scrim of electricity vibrated above her like a bat wing and prickled the skin on her arms. Even before her hair rose to greet the static created by the creature's twisting appendages, she noticed the quiver in her eyelashes and her fine brows. The minute down on her arms rose—every feather of her being rushed to encounter his.

Slowly, sensors lit and hovered. Something moved in her periphery, so she turned. The depth of the room was in deep shadow with darkness crowding the corners. Myriad jointed arms extended as if to greet her. Celia knew the creature before she gave him a name. She had seen the drawings and typed up the narratives from the scribbles surrounding the schematics. One night she had unearthed her brother's battered collection of comic books after translating the engineer's drawings all day. Celia remembered rolling her eyes at the fantasy aspect, but she could grasp the theoretical beginnings of it. This machine was a masterpiece on the drawing board, but in fact? Where was the chief engineer? Where was Dr. Tregoning?

"Hello?" She took a step forward and watched the extensions recoil. Tregoning had blathered about robots replacing human workers when he labored past exhaustion and drank from the bottle hidden in his desk. The company wanted an untiring, self-sufficient workforce capable of twenty-four-hour-a-day production. She blinked into the sensors poised at eye-level—here it was.

"Dr. Tregoning? It's Celia Maycomb." Celia ground her teeth thinking of the selfishness of the company accountants promoted to the president's office at the poultry processing plant. How many more chicken farms were needed to support such an endeavor? A job was a job, which was her only reason for working at the plant that belched an acrid, mealy odor over her little town. Her lips curled.

More lights on other appendages engaged and lit up the room at floor level. This robot was the most complex she had ever seen. Of course, there were small areas of the plant that were mechanized, but each machine needed the human overseer. Most rendered the product ready for human assembly.

This creature was certainly the product of the research manifestos that she had massaged into a few bound manuals kept in a locked file drawer. Her knowledge from the reports could not be discounted--he had trusted her to keep his secrets. She had signed the non-disclosure agreements and then scribed each file for the private archives kept for future consideration. How much cyber-thieving was there in this particular business? Was there truly the threat of intellectual piracy among the chicken nugget manufacturers of the world? She had categorized the research, the lab experiments, and their results as wild, cerebral driveling. Dr. Drew Tregoning, her immediate boss and one of the most prolific engineers of the Castro Poultry's research office, channeled the mad scientist at times.

Celia mentally shook her head to toss out all prior knowledge and misinformation. She had automatically craned her neck, arched her back slightly and widened her eyes, though instinct cautioned hunching her body into protection of soft tissue like the eyes, cheeks, and softly parted lips. She closed her mouth the moment she noticed her image in the monitor attached to the wall across from the door she had entered moments ago. She had simply pressed on the previously hidden door, crossed the threshold without the expected alarm sounding, and closed it with a surreptitious tug. Inside the cavernous, dark room, she wondered why she had gained entry with so little effort.

The blank, gray door at the end of the long hallway which ended her floor's suite of offices had tempted her during her first week at the plant. No doorknob, no plaque like the rest of the series of locked doors, and no one venturing in or out. A closet? A sealed area? When she first examined the door there hadn't been scratch marks on the sill--marks that originated from the other side. Now ominous gouges marked the wood threshold, and a slug-like trail gleamed from the door and ended in the middle of the cavernous room.

Months ago, Tregoning had given Celia a lengthy journal that might have birthed this creature hovering and whirring right above her head. The glut of work had distracted her during the entire ninety-day trial period for new employees and had lulled her into entertained complacence. The essays were sometimes lab notes written out in paragraphs that sounded like monologues as she typed and edited. The work was focused on robotics and the possibility of a fully automated plant that could repair itself as parts jammed, broke, or malfunctioned. The historic malfunctions described were often labeled the "human element" because, simply put, human beings are not dependable when under pressure. Machines were more efficient.

Four nights ago, Tregoning had disappeared down the hallway and had not reemerged. Celia silently scoffed when one of the other supervisors mentioned that Drew Tregoning was extending his stay in Caribbean for a tech conference. There was no tech conference in the Caribbean or anywhere between the doctor's walk past her cubicle one evening and his complete vaporization. She mused that there should never be lies in research—just fact piled onto fact in a ponderous line that sequentially told a story, solved a problem, or equated into some truth. Research created something like this fantastic creature tumbling and whirring its extensions fast enough to maintain a static charge in the air around her person.

Celia blinked out of theory when she saw herself on a monitor. What was this thing? A prototype? A plaything? A pretend vacation from reality? There was one optical extension poised an arm-length from her face, but the monitor showed her from many angles, so she concluded that there were many more lenses. The zoom hovered close and then backed away. The picture on the screen broke into multiple images—one in three dimensions and in another, a thermal reading in which her body was shaded a surreal, fuzzy green-blue swirled with tinges of red in the face, chest and belly. Numbers ran in a ticker down the screen at the right edge that she assumed were respiration, heart rate, and temperature. Some of the numbers were stated in algorithms that begged her to study. Celia opened and closed her eyes to break out of petrified wonder.

"My name is Celia Maycomb." The arms danced in reaction, and Celia's hair rose in silvery-blond strands of attention from her scalp. She resisted the urge to smooth them down. As a rule of thumb, she made no fast moves on barking dogs, angry men, or curious scientific experiments. That thought quirked her lips.

A voice boomed, "Cecelia Jane Maycomb. Office C42. No clearance." Unconsciously, Celia's shoulders drooped a bit. The voice was tinny and flat. She continued to gaze upward and count extensions—seven, which stopped at a uniform distance from her and took readings and adjusted in a quick-motion jerkiness. When she imagined such a creature, the appendages moved smoothly, and the processing was instantaneous.

Celia rolled her eyes at the automaton, "The door opened the moment I touched it. And only my mother calls me Cecelia. I'll leave you alone then." She turned toward the door and felt the first prickle of fear course up her spine. The door had disappeared, and where it might have been, another monitor blinked a stream of numbers. Seven appendages surrounded her while warning computations arced through her brain: optical, taste, tactile, olfactory, and auditory. What else? Temperature, perhaps? What other types of sensory devices would she design for such a creature? There had been one odd study on extrasensory perception that had been out of step with the rest of research on bees, the human nervous system, artificial intelligence, and fusion models.

The voice spoke right into her ear and made her jump. "Celia Maycomb. Clearance granted. Stay." The tumble of arms pulled back and lured her forward. The blinks of tiny bulbs in one drew her to lean in to see it better. Booming, the voice warned, "Do not touch. Touch hurts."

Celia nodded as her eyes widened at the possibilities. "I work with Drew Tregoning. Where is he?" The clicks above her buzzed in a hive of processing. She counted on her fingers before it answered. Processing was slowed to seconds when saving new information. In her periphery, the optic monitor showed the quiver of her fingers keeping track of the moments. She stilled her fingers. The machine was studying her reactions. She had edited Tregoning's essay on the revelations of eye blinks, lid movement, and other facial muscle contraction. He had unlocked the secrets of the iris, which she had found interesting, if speculative. Had he taught the creature the same methods of divining human intention? "What foolishness," she muttered.

"Touch hurts," the voice intoned. Then the tone shifted toward conclusion, "Touch hurts humans." Silence followed the declaration.

Celia slowed her breathing, and her hair descended from its ascent chasing electrocution. She made her eyes remain steady and steely. She looked straight into the monitor because it was human to look at the appendages of a strange creature and fail to look it in the eye. "I won't touch you then. Where is Drew Tregoning?" She held her breath then panted a bit to throw off the parts tracking her expulsion of carbon dioxide. She immediately felt a breath of air brush by her arm as some unseen air duct opened.

"Follow the light." The finality of the blank voice struck her. A cold lump of fear lodged in her throat. Curiosity had delivered her through the gray door at the end of the hallway on her own floor. Curiosity vanquished; all Celia truly desired was escape. She turned toward the series of spotlights that bounced off the dull, gray floor and forced her feet to move. Perhaps there was an exit like the glowing red sign under the screen at the theater that beaconed release from danger.

Before she reached the dark square at the far end of the warehouse-sized expanse, she asked the creature one more question, "Did Dr. Tregoning's touch hurt you?"

"You." The word baffled it.

"What does the doctor call you? What is your name?" Dimly in the gloom of the dark warehouse, she saw a form on a bed about thirty feet away. As she continued forward, she noted that he was sprawled limply either in sleep or death. When she was less than ten feet from the bed, she saw numbers displayed atop the outline of a body on a smaller monitor. She wondered if they reflected his shallow respiration and a very slow heart rate. Could a human survive under thirty beats per minute? Brain activity—perhaps the seventh appendage monitored brain activity because a very faint gray pulse beat in the scanned creature's head. Hers had been red and swirling—perhaps it hadn't been a simple thermal image but a combination of thermals, brain activity, and body functions.

Again, the processing time lengthened with the new query, her movement, and The processing time lengthened as Celia moved toward the man lying inert on the bare mattress. As she bent to touch the doctor, the creature boomed, "Touch hurts."

Celia straightened and frowned at the twitching, metal arm that hesitated to pull her back from their pet. She shook her head, "Humans touch each other. Touch does not always hurt." She sighed and took another breath for patience. "Did something go wrong when he touched you?"

"Do not touch. Touch hurts." The appendages crowded between Celia and Tregoning.

She cast her mind to distracting it. "What is your name?" She wanted to stamp her foot in a burst of impatience to scare the creature away like a wild animal.

"Serial number LX."

She cocked her head and thought about their dilemma. The man on the bed released a huge sigh and made her impulsive. "LX? As in sixty in Latin? How about Alex?" The man on the bed turned his head toward her voice and groaned.

Celia lowered herself to squatting by the mattress-like platform. She peered through the barrier of the creature's probes. Tregoning's limp body draped a stage-like box, not a mattress. This raised box kept him off the cement floor about three feet. Cold emanated from the gray, dull surface of the unfinished cement.

The doctor's whiskers looked grown out a few days but not the nearly four he'd been missing. The rest of his face was the milk-gray of oatmeal, and the odor of scorched cotton hung about him. Celia wondered if that spoke of partial electrocution.

Sweet. Celia had never been irritated enough with the man to wish him harm, but others in the department had poked fun at his wild theories behind his back. Drew Tregoning was "going trés mad," one of the assistants had mocked. This man looked as if he had been twisted into a knot and dropped on the platform. She leaned over to observe without touching him as the creature's arms flashed but parted to hover in her periphery. His fingertips on the exposed right hand were blistered as if burned, and his socks looked worn through just on the bottoms. What had happened? Malfunction? A program error?

The man who used to be Dr. Andrew Tregoning, the mad theorist and condescending genius of the Castro's research office, moved his head and opened bloodshot eyes. They narrowed to distress and instant alarm. "Maycomb?" His voice croaked from disuse. "Leave."

The creature's arms whirled and dipped. Celia felt her hair make contact with one flailing appendage and sizzle in a flash of tinder and then crumble.

"Doctor! Hush!" She cast an eye to the other arms that might crowd her if she didn't control panic. She summoned up anger, "Stay back, Alex. Touch hurts. Do not touch me."

She sucked in a breath and ignored the man who had rolled over and lay with his eyes wide and panicked. How long had he been rendered insensible by the creature through an inadvertent touch? She opened and closed her eyes. She focused on the extended arm of the centipede-like optical probe with its hundreds of tiny camera lense. The monitor was flashing a dizzying ballet of dueling images featuring two human outlines. "Doctor? Alex allowed me to enter the lab. Alex is concerned about your condition."

"Alex?" She watched the doctor recover full consciousness, though his eyes reflected the blended images of LX's probes recording every nuance of her lion-like appearance with the extended froth of long, gold and silver hair and enormous amber-flecked, green eyes. He blinked up at her in shock, but then his eyes narrowed on her purposefully widening and narrowing eyes. She tried Morse code to goad him into movement. Her mouth curved into a smirk as she abandoned the message "M-O-V-E." She blinked more boldly, "G-E-T U-P I-D-I-O-T."

Celia watched Drew Tregoning summon every bit of reserve strength and force himself to the edge of the platform. He extended a hand with all the nails peeled back; Celia assumed the injury came when he tried to claw open the door. The tactile probe had burned right through his pants and fused his socks to his ankle. dragging him to the back of the lab and tossing him onto the platform where the final assembly must have taken place during a late-night whim.

Celia stared at the bloodied hand and realized the reason for the gouges on the threshold. She hoped the ankle with the burned sock wasn't broken. She glanced back to the monitor that recorded every expression on her face. Tears sprang to her eyes out of fear, but she whispered, "Touch does hurt. Alex, I must help Drew to the door. I must take him to a human doctor."

"What is that?" the robot asked. The tactile probe extended a thin plastic cylinder that Celia allowed to touch the moisture that she had wiped off her cheeks with one finger.

"Tears. I am afraid." She looked at the place where the door had been and then back to the injured man. "I am afraid he will die."

"Die?"

"Cease to exist. No power. Non-existence." Celia straightened from her squat beside the platform. She moved with deliberate slowness.

Drew watched her gain most of the computer's attention with her masses of live-wire hair reacting to the static energy building in the room. She tried not to talk her way into a quagmire—trying to shut the thing down must have created this catastrophe. It was miraculous that had she managed to gain entrance without electrocution. She had found the hidden door and stayed alive long enough to find him.

Alex stilled, and her hair began to settle like a cloud. "Non-existence. Touch hurts." The whirling began again the moment she shook her head. The static in the air arced through the upper area near the high ceiling.

Celia was not deterred. "He will not die if I take him to the doctor. Humans can touch humans."

"No. Touch hurts." The brain in the creature must be learning at warp speed in some areas, but interpersonal interactions were lagging.

Celia shook her head and reached over to Drew Tregoning and cupped his left cheek. She looked over at the monitor and saw frozen images of the red heat of sharing touch. The appendages were hovering closer than a foot in a hot metal atmosphere of wary protection.

She tried not to wince when she smelled more of her hair singeing to ash. She looked into Drew's large, frightened eyes and pursed her lips. "You owe me a haircut after the trip to the hospital, Dr. Tregoning."

Celia Maycomb dropped her hand to pull the unsteady man closer to the edge of the platform. She spoke to the creature as she pulled the doctor up to sitting. "Alex? Did touching Doctor Tregoning hurt you also?"

The whirr of the appendages grew to a buzzing hive as Celia positioned herself under Tregoning's left arm and grabbed his belt with her right. She helped him hoist himself upright and begin to lurch across the empty warehouse.

Discarded boxes littered the left side of the space, but other than monitors and one large lab table and chair near the door, only the platform populated the space. About halfway across the room, Drew sagged for a moment. She hung onto him as he panted and let his burned foot rest on the floor with a shudder. His fingertips were bleeding on the hand gripping her shoulder. His weakness betrayed more damage than the obvious burns and breaks in extremities.

The creature finally answered when they started to shamble across the floor toward the invisible door. "Touch hurts, Celia. Protect Alex. No touch." The voice had learned intonation from analyzing her few words. She noticed it intoned "Alex" like she did with a slight stress on the first syllable. She wanted to grin at Tregoning—she wanted to gloat. A few minutes with his creature and she had taught it something. A dozen feet away, the outline of the door gleamed gray against the blackness in the glow of a hovering bulb. The monitor angled crookedly streamed color and waves of code.

Looking upward as they reached the door, Celia impelled the stumbling Tregoning over the marred threshold. She turned to bid Alex farewell. The bulb over the door was joined by a dozen more. Her throat closed as the true expanse of the creature revealed itself in the carnival of static racing across the ceiling like a miniature electric storm. Every rack of computer processors, any leftover monitors, and over a hundred probe-like arms hovered in a mask of the true ceiling like foam insulation.

Alex had protected himself from touch and discovery. He had allowed Celia to remove the dangerous man who threatened existence. Touch hurt. Touch led to self-protection. Celia looked back at the man she saved from his monstrous creation. She wondered why she had saved him.

Celia Works a Conundrum

"The foot? Bad sprain." Tregoning's voice hadn't recovered from his supposed trip to the Caribbean symposium on fusion models for robotic manufacturing. When he spoke, the rattle sounded like an engine sputtering.

The other man was trying to tease more from the doctor who looked too white, gaunt and serious to have just returned from a tropical anything. The big man blustered, "Well, it must have been a real adventure to end up in a cast. You look positively done in, Andrew. And your hand!" First hour of the new workday and the big boss was doubting Tregoning's thin lie.

Celia huffed into the room after picking up a random file folder and stuffing it with a report she'd pulled on the optics of a bumblebee versus the brown recluse spider. After her audience with the fiercest recluse spider king of them all, Celia found that odd study fascinating. After her audience with the undisputed king of the Castro Research, Celia discovered that she was a voracious reader of formerly dry reports on fusion models in miniature, the analysis of eye movement in humans and recent discoveries concerning thermal imaging. Evidently, Celia's Irish grandmother had not been so daffy after all—you could read a person by the aura they produced. Celia wondered if her aura was pitch black as she descended on the two men locked in a silent battle of seek and avoid.

She forced a giggle, "Good morning, Mr. Champion! Dr. Tregoning? That report you wanted to review before your," she made a show of checking her watch, "eight-thirty appointment with Mr. Alex." She placed the folder on his desk and arched a brow at the older, barrel-chested man who was still attractive despite age and added girth. She leaned toward the man and lowered her voice, "I hear that Dr. Tregoning hardly left his room. I hear he was tangled up . . ." she trailed off as Tregoning shouted, "Out!" Champion chuckled.

Celia congratulated herself when she heard Tregoning, sounding a bit more human, growl out, "She's spreading rumors of bedroom hijinks because I fail to tan. Women!" He raised his voice theatrically, "She'd better focus on the job, not my personal life."

Celia Maycomb saunter back down the hallway swinging her hips. She tossed her shortened hair. Mr. Champion should be curious, she thought, with his lead scientist missing for days and then returning injured. She frowned at other details the management failed to notice like the shipments of components for the creature and the electricity it must burn to run the thing. How had the funding been secured for such a creature as the one inhabiting the warehouse? The technology alone would climb into the millions.

She tried to imagine Andrew Tregoning assembling the entire wobbly structure that comprised Alex and frowned. He must have had a team, but where were they now? She stood at one of the few windows looking out onto the parking lot. The shift had changed a half hour ago, but only a few employees still milled about talking. There was talk of layoffs. There were no extraneous employees. No. There hadn't been a team, she realized. First, you build a robot that is capable of fixing itself—a machine that learns, masters, and seeks information. Give the creature the tools and let the thing evolve.

She bit her lip; it was the old problem of the petri dish: you can mix the same ingredients and get startlingly different results if any of the variables change. Timing, temperature, amount of light, and chance aberrations affect the product. Think of crops. Look at children. How about those pesky snowflakes, tornadoes, and hurricanes? The creature had overbuilt itself like the athlete addicted to steroids. Anger, fear, and paranoia had bred with the toxicity of unleashed genius.

Later, Doctor Tregoning struggled into her cubicle and lowered himself into the chair before her desk. He was so exhausted, she thought he might fall asleep before he spoke. "Stop making up stories. We were the laughingstock at the hospital."

"Hiding in here to wait out your 8:30 appointment?" Celia ignored his irritation. She had caught him chuckling after she amused the examining room with her bawdy explanation for his injuries. She had been waiting for this man to become human for nearly four months, and now he was some cross between pitiful and insane. Rather irritating and scary.

He nodded and closed his eyes. He grumbled, "What an odd angel, you are, Celia." She grinned thinking of the way she had rambled on telling fibs to the attending physician who was apt to wander off and make them wait.

She had managed to catch the attention of the doctor, the nurse, and the entire housekeeping staff. Channeling a bit of a southern drawl, she had pretended to confide in the intern, "Look. I think his foot is broken from bearing all his weight. She had him shackled upside down as far as I can tell. Poor man dragged himself across the room and ruined his fingers on the balcony ledge trying to get away from her. That's what you get when you hire a tramp for the night. Right, Drew?" A nurse smirked over Celia's musing over the use of a cattle prod or a stun gun when the doctor asked about the burn wounds. The doctor's injuries tallied two cracked ribs, four points of scorching from electric shock, and a badly sprained ankle. His hands were a mess, but they were just rubbed raw and bruised with a few fingernails broken to their beds.

Tregoning pressed the fingers on his unbandaged hand to his forehead. "It's probably written on some chart at the hospital that I'm a deviant."

"I'd rather be suspected as such than caught with Alex." Celia felt her humor fading.

"If I felt better, I might drag you down the hall and toss you back inside with your Alex."

"He's the true prisoner of the Castro Research. What are you going to do?"

"Shhhh," he looked out her door. "You are going to ruin my reputation," he rasped.

She shook her head—the man was known as too serious, dull, and impervious. "How did you manage that door? It just disappears."

He raised his head and squinted at her curiosity. "Chinese puzzle box design. My father brought a few back from Korea with a collection of figures and dolls that my grandmother treasured." He shook his head. "You are too curious, Miss Maycomb, but last night, I'm glad you were curious enough to find me." He stared at her hair. "You looked like an angel with your hair all full of static." He frowned, "How old are you?"

Celia blinked and angled her head as if using her sharp eyes to take a thermal reading of him. His forehead might be vibrant orange for the bloom of a headache chasing around the front of his skull. She noticed that at ten feet. "Thirty-five. And you?"

"Forty-two. I never thought about your age—I assumed you were twenty-two like all the other beginning researchers." He was blunt and a bit suspicious. "How did you know there was a door at the end of the hallway? How did you know where to look for me?"

She was concentrating on his processing that was much faster than the creature's last night. "The door was always there. The first week I was working here I noticed it. And I wasn't exactly looking for you."

"That door is invisible to the naked eye."

"Hardly. Granted that geometric rearrangement when you touch it at dead center is genius, but the door is fairly obvious. And I saw you go down the hall and not reappear on Monday nearly two weeks ago. Where else would you go?" Celia pouted, "There was no conference in the Caribbean last week."

Tregoning frowned so deeply, the crease between his eyes furrowed. "True. There was no conference, symposium or workshop." His voice fell to bitterness. "There was one mistake heaped on another and another until that creature you've dubbed 'Alex' spouted wings and took off."

"What did you expect from artificial intelligence? Learning and performing is part of his programming." She was jotting notes on a white legal-size pad. She flashed him a sketch of what she had seen during her exploration of the secret lab at the end of the hall. He watched her sketch the details and her guesses at the content of some of the square boxes, the cylinders that collected data and the blinking read-outs from probes too miniscule to house monitors or processors.

She looked up and caught him staring at her sketch. She angled it toward him, "What did you expect, Doctor? You decided to act the creator and assembled the first unit. What is step two?"

Tregoning shook his head. "That is the classic programmer question. Your intention qualifies me as a scientist instead of a true madman. There was no plan. Activation was like striking the flint in the presence of alcohol fumes or the sudden release of gas pent up in a house ready to explode." He shrugged. "The computer immolated and changed within eye blinks. I never even thought to stop it as it assembled itself without any further assistance." He sighed but looked as if he might begin to cry. "Why was I so surprised that it would quibble when I decided to flip the kill switch and end the experiment for the night?"

Carol Casey

LOVE LETTER TO THE BOHEMIA RIVER

Summer is your season, tranquil your reign
over the wide basin where narrow creeks co-mingle.
In your shallows, herons haul in smallmouth bass.
Among reeds, raccoons clean up dinner. Slalom skiers,
solemn swimmers, hopeful fishers casting for a rock.
All these worship you.

Eyes on the sky, you flow beyond the span.
The strait deepens, cleaves, gives you over
to the turgid Elk, buff-toned river of commerce
and thick-mudded floor.

The ancient story. Persephone must descend.
We know your end yet yearn for your beginnings—
recall you with a sigh, on our way somewhere,
crossing that old bridge.

Laura Shovan

DANAE ADDRESSES COVID-19

There were days before my father-king
ordered me to shelter in this chamber,
when I sat all morning on the harbor wall.
It was not the ships nor their sails
which drew my gaze, but the way light fell—
almost solid —and broke the water's surface.
I remember the sun had muscle,
gold as the shoulders of a swimmer.
This I conceived long ago. Enter
if you must, god of fevers. Bring to me
the morning light, that first rush
of heat rubbing my eyelids open.

Carol Casey

RELENTLESS MARCH

Waves
   snake sinuous
on shore,
   cold as blood.

Off the point,
   white-cap orcas,
    break water
ravage wind.

The world   in quarantine
   every house   supposed a haven.
      Harboring.

Cheryl Sadowski

ONLY CONNECT

1910

Only connect! That was the whole of her sermon. Only connect the prose and the passion, and both will be exalted, and human love will be seen at its height. Live in fragments no longer. Only connect, and the beast and the monk, robbed of the isolation that is life to either, will die.
—E.M. Forster, Howard's End

March 2020

Friday the 13th is too obvious a date, and too ominous. So it is either Wednesday, March 11th or Thursday, March 12th when I leave the office with a feeling that things are getting weird, that I might not be back for a little while. The spread of the novel coronavirus has taken hold in the news and in the national consciousness, though the World Health Organization is yet to declare a pandemic.

I am halfway across the stone courtyard of my office building before remembering that I left my laptop at my desk. I backtrack through the courtyard and ride the elevator to the fourth floor to retrieve it in the event my office closes for a few days. Then I go grocery shopping (just in case). An air of anxiety hangs over depleted supplies of fruits and vegetables. In the bread aisle loaves lie strewn about the floor as people sift urgently through the shelves.

One loaf looks particularly sad and deflated, its middle flattened by the wheel of a shopping cart. The image sticks in my mind as I drive home, wondering what kind of frenzy turns bread loaves into casualties in its wake.

1917

On March 8, 1917, demonstrators clamoring for bread took to the streets in the Russian capital of Petrograd (now known as St. Petersburg). Supported by 90,000 men and women on strike, the protesters clashed with police but refused to leave the streets. On March 10, the strike spread among all of Petrograd's workers and irate mobs of workers destroyed police stations.

—*This Day in History*, History.com

1981

I am fifteen when my parents take me to see the movie *Reds*. I have been inducted into the tradition of epic films from an early age, so it is not unusual for me to hold up for a three-hour love story that unfolds amid grand historical events.

The messy, creative, bohemian lives of writers and lovers John Reed and Louise Bryant appeal to me. I marvel at their courage and willingness to be swept into the current of their times. Writing and reporting from the front lines of the Russian Revolution in the fall of 1917 was not for the faint of heart.

Reds romanticizes social unrest through sweeping, sepia-toned filmography—there are hopeful ballads, political rallies, the crunch of boots in snow-laden streets. The movie theater, a double-decker, is packed. When the credits finally roll the audience breaks into applause. For a moment there is human electricity in the air—the kind of invisible connection that comes from shared experience.

1918

PUBLIC NOTICE
Treasury Department, United States Public Health Service
INFLUENZA:
Spread by Droplets sprayed from Nose and Throat
Cover each COUGH and SNEEZE with handkerchief
Spread by contact.
AVOID CROWDS.
If possible, WALK TO WORK.
Do not spit on the floor or sidewalk.
Do not use common drinking cups and common towels.
Avoid excessive fatigue.
If taken ill, go to bed and send for a doctor.
The above applies to colds, bronchitis, pneumonia, and tuberculosis.

1985

In my senior year of high school, I make an unusual choice to eschew the camaraderie of after-school sports for a job shelving books at the regional library. Working amid the stacks, lulled by the library's hushed tones and soft window light, is reverie for me. The Dewey Decimal system appeals to my sense of order. The librarians appreciate my eagerness to talk with patrons about the books they are seeking.

But I am a plodding docent, examining the dust jackets and opening the pages of each volume before fitting it snugly into its home on the shelf. Time permeates the library, the steady progression of clocks, the ponderous advancement of my cart down carpeted aisles. I pay attention to the books I handle; through them, Time reveals itself as an invisible yarn that spindles between subjects. Biographies connect with periods in history, history intersects with literature, art, and science. Book after book, cart by cart, hour upon hour, I see the threads of the world, woven together like a dense rug.

1918

After the flu, I was a pretty lonely kid. All my friends had died. These were the friends I had played with for years, gone to school with. When I lost them, my whole world changed. People didn't seem as friendly as before, they didn't visit each other, bring food over, have parties all the time. The neighborhood changed. People changed. Everything changed.

—John Delano, New Haven, Connecticut, *Influenza 1918*

April 2020

More than 2,000 American are dying every day from Covid-19. More than a million are infected with the coronavirus. *The Washington Post* calls the disease a "swift executioner" and describes "bodies stacked, mothers and fathers discarded in bags piled onto refrigerator trucks in hospital parking lots."

Nature appears blithely ignorant, even cruel in its determination to bloom in accord with the season: showy azaleas, magenta magnolia buds, white-star crabapple blossoms with feathery centers. Everything is buzzing, humming, hovering, *alive*—even the cobalt blue spring sky. To read the news and look outside is cognitive dissonance as death plaits together with the vibrant, palpable spring.

Fear and beauty make odd bedfellows.

1951

What makes loneliness so unbearable is the loss of one's own self, which can be realized in solitude, but confirmed in its identity only by the trusting and trustworthy company of my equals. In this situation, man loses trust in himself as the partner of his thoughts and that elementary confidence in the world which is necessary to make experiences...

—Hannah Arendt, *The Origins of Totalitarianism*

2020

I am not a healthcare provider or an essential worker, but a nonprofit marketing professional who adapts a basement back room into an office where I work five days a week for an indeterminable time. There is a window that overlooks a grove of trees and a lawn. During Zoom conference calls I see groundhogs, squirrels, hawks, and deer. I am acutely aware of the advantage and the perquisites of my situation. Meanwhile exhausted doctors, nurses, and grocery store workers brave the front lines to outmaneuver a capricious enemy they do not understand and cannot see.

Because I am no longer commuting to work, I gain back two hours each day. In the early morning or late afternoon I take up E.M. Forster's *Howard's End*. It is a lush novel about three families: the commercially successful Wilcoxes, the scholarly and artistic Schlegels, and the poverty-stricken Basts. Though their lives become intertwined in permanent ways, their ability to relate and connect with one another remains elusive. The story unfolds amid imagery of encroaching development, frequent train travel, social and cultural longing—all metaphors for the corrosive effects of technology and capitalism upon home, hearth, and most of all, belonging.

During the day, my phone lights up with alerts about the rampant spread of the coronavirus. My colleagues and I stare across digital divides that blunt our expressions. Fear and anxiety are universal, yet amid the absence of body language and a direct gaze it is hard to discern, until one of our voices breaks, or our eyes well up.

Zoom squares are neat and clean; they encase emotion so that it cannot spill over.

May 2020

George Floyd is killed on a street in Minneapolis on May 25. I watch the video twice: once, because I need to see it, then again because I want the horror to imprint itself upon my brain, to slap me out of my fog. Floyd's death does what nothing else has been able to: it transcends the coronavirus andit shatters the digital dome under which white-collar workers like myself are living. It wakens America to its sins and deficiencies.

2015

The civic commons, the places we share with the rest of society, are where interaction underpins opportunity and democracy. While cities continue to fulfill this critical role, there is compelling evidence that the connective tissue that binds us together is coming apart. In particular, it appears the level of social capital—the connections and norms of reciprocity that smooth interpersonal actions and support community—has declined in the United States over several decades.

—Joe Cortright, "Less in Common," *City Report,* cityobservatory.com

July 2020

The New York Times reports at least 150,000 people have died from the coronavirus at a rate of roughly 1,000 deaths per week. Unprecedented numbers of Americans resort to food banks as the pandemic spawns mass unemployment.

George Floyd solidarity protests erupt in major U.S. cities and suburbs. Some demonstrations are violent as unidentified, camouflaged federal agents clash with citizens in public streets and spaces.

In some parts of the country the heat indexes have reached triple digits in one of the warmest Julys on record.

Alchemy is change, it requires heat.

I look at my calendar to see that I have four Zoom meetings scheduled this afternoon. Outside, the sound of cicadas. Normally a delightful harbinger of the season, their low, constant din reminds me of a buzzing fiber optic network in this summer of discontent.

Ellen Krawczak

FEAR RETURNS

I wonder what is happening to my body now that I am afraid and under stress again. I've been afraid before but generally only for a very short period of time. I was frightened when there was a fire in my office building and the exit stairwell was blocked by smoke, and again when someone tried to break into my apartment while I was sleeping. My heart quickened and I became hypervigilant, ready for flight. But those instances were over quickly, my heart rate dropped down to normal, my breathing slowed, and life went on as before.

But I have also known sustained fear. In the fall of 2002, snipers John Allen Muhammad, and Lee Boyd Malvo went on a killing spree in northern Virginia, Washington, D.C., and Montgomery County. They terrorized the public with their random killings and before they were caught they had killed seventeen people and injured others. The first killing in the Baltimore Washington area occurred on October 2, when a man was murdered in Montgomery County while crossing a Shoppers Food Warehouse parking lot. The next day a woman was killed at a post office and witnesses reported seeing a white van or truck. The police asked the public to be on the alert.

I was working in Montgomery County at that time. The office staff heard the news bulletin but no one was particularly alarmed. However, when a white box truck showed up in the parking lot across from our office building and no one exited the truck, I called the police. The police approached the truck quietly and very cautiously. The driver had only pulled over to take a snooze. Then suddenly there were more killings – a woman vacuuming her van at a gas station, a bus driver inside his commuter bus, a landscaper mowing the lawn. The office staff stopped going out to lunch, stopped running errands or shopping during their break. People were afraid to be out, afraid to go to the gas station or grocery shopping.

And I was afraid too. I was living alone, and although I lived in an adjacent county, no one could be sure when or where the snipers would show up. I worried when I arrived home to an empty house, I worried when I had to go out. I worried as I drove to work and I worried when I drove home. I was late to work one morning because the police had set up a roadblock and were checking everyone's cars. It wasn't as if I was frightened out of my wits all the time–I wasn't. But there was the dull ache of fear that accompanied me wherever I went. I wasn't sure how the stress was affecting me, but I was sure that the stress was taking a toll on my body.

Today, the worry about stress affecting my body has returned.

October 2002, with its colorful leaves, brought the sniper along with the last warm weather of fall. April 2020, when I was voluntarily quarantined, brought the deadly coronavirus and the first hint of spring and warm weather. Yet, I am always cold, cold due to the fear that is snaking through my body. This is how my body responds when I'm afraid. Eighteen years ago, I was alert for any strange noises in the house–did the snipers follow me home, are they lurking in the woods behind my house? Today, I am alert for any changes in my body–do I have a fever, am I slightly out of breath?

Now that dull ache is back. I am afraid because I am considered high risk, afraid that if I catch the coronavirus I might pass it on to Jim and my family. I am not ready to die.

The snipers were the unknown enemy; no one knew who they were or where they would strike. It is ironic that if I catch the virus it might be from someone I know. Will I catch it from a friend? Will one of my grandchildren be asymptomatic and pass it on to me? Will I breathe in little particles from the person standing in line in front of me at the farmers market?

The isolation is crippling. Only when I walk outside do I truly connect with other people. People wave as they pass me on their bikes, or say hello as I walk through the neighborhood. I see their faces without masks, I hear their voices and I feel that once again I am part of a community. But still, the virus is out there and I know that I must be very careful. Many of my friends are starting to drift back to a more normal routine–meeting at a restaurant to play mah-jongg, having lunch or dinner with a group outdoors. I too am slowly getting back to meeting a friend for lunch or a walk, meeting in small groups in the open air. I am still trying to reconcile that life the way I lived it might never come back. Going to exercise and line dancing classes three days a week in the gym, dining in restaurants, hosting dinner parties--all those things might be gone for a very long time.

How do I balance my life between being careful and living? How do I respond to that loss of control? What happens in the fall when it is flu season? And will I be living like this into the winter and early spring? I miss my friends and family who live in other states and wonder if I will see them again. I miss seeing my children and grandchildren. I miss traveling and hope that we will be able to go on the vacation next year that was originally planned for this year. I miss my old life, but that is also now part of my past. I tell myself to exercise regularly, to eat well, to stay in touch with those I love. I tell myself to adjust and adapt. I tell myself to "live."

Christopher T. George

ASSATEAGUE IN THE TIME OF COVID-19

The ponies refuse to perform for us;
mosquitoes possess no such scruples.
Mare and colt graze on the salt marsh
a half mile off as we socially distance.

*(A gander hisses as you nosily point your
camera at his cutely plumed goslings.)*

On the beach, beyond the battlements of dunes,
Mister and Missus Baltimore sun their pectorals,
their jazzy Maryland flag anti-virus masks strung
from ears as they slurp their hot dogs and sloppy Joes.

The teen guys in their red Corvette, recklessly maskless,
boom boom their bass notes as they careen through
the pebbled parking lot by Tom's Cove as they hunt
well-filled bikinis. Meanwhile, you find a tiny pile of sun-

bleached bones, unnamable bones, possibly bird,
fish, or mammal, your lithe fingers the perfect
ossuary as you cherish those precious bones just
as the Assateague Indians guarded theirs, fleshed
and unfleshed, from the uninvited depredations
of Colonel Edmund Scarborough, who attempted
to exterminate them four centuries ago yet found them
harder to find than conquer. So, the Assateague performed

their own funeral rites, not Scarborough's, driving
flesh from bone, to leave a simple prayer of bone.

Karen Kendra

MY PANDEMIC WISH LIST

It's the end of July 2020, and more than four months since my husband and I isolated ourselves from most of the world in fear of Covid-19. Our last planned social gathering was in March, when we hoped to host a St. Patrick's Day dinner party. Out of the sixteen friends we invited, only five of us sat around the green-clothed table, which was arrayed with Irish food and spirits. The warnings about the pandemic had come late, but were finally official and people were starting to stay home.

Since then, my world has been narrowed to brief trips to the supermarket or occasional drives with my husband in our sealed car with few stops where there are no crowds of people capable of infecting us. I feel as though I inhabit one of those horror movies where the characters cast suspicious glances over their shoulders lest they be overtaken by whatever evil force threatens.

Today, as I watched the televised drama of a horse-drawn carriage carry the flag-draped coffin of U.S. House Representative John R. Lewis over the Edmund Pettus Bridge in Selma, AL, I wept for this heroic man. Then, I was suddenly ashamed of my whining about our personal social limitations during the pandemic. Lewis walked across that bridge in 1965 with Martin Luther King and hundreds of others toward armed enforcers of racial discrimination and brutality just to gain the right to vote as they had been promised by the constitution. Despite the letter of the law, blacks were still thwarted at the polls, as they are even now, three amendments later.

Lewis and others were attacked and beaten by the police who were hired to protect the people---though not black people. And even now, though their journey resulted in the Voting Rights Act of 1965, forces of suppression and discrimination are still at work.

Lewis spent his life fighting for the right to vote freely, among many other issues he brought before our congressional representatives. He was called the "Conscience of the Congress." His torch has now passed to another generation of many colors, not just black.

While I am "safe" in my masked and sanitized world of retirement and affluence, millions of our countrymen are facing something akin to a Four Horsemen of the Pandemic--plague, unemployment, starvation, and possible eviction from their homes.

Amidst those are the continuing protests against racial injustice incited by the brutal on-camera murder of a black man more than two months ago. The protestors are now being met in opposition by federal troops. The Black Lives Matter movement was formed several years ago after a similar incident, but which was without the televised horror. Outraged, people of all colors have joined that movement and fill the streets of our nation.

I have little to complain about for myself. But I do have a wish list for our country.

I wish people did not equate wearing a mask with weakness or a political statement, but as an effective gesture of good will and concern for their fellow citizens.

I wish that Congress would act as though their families are as threatened by eviction, food challenges, occupational, and medical issues as a majority of their constituents are.

I wish that the peaceful protestors who continue to represent those of us who cannot participate will remain strong, vocal, and nonviolent so that the cause they so passionately support will not be tainted by anarchist interlopers.

I wish that all our police functioned as protectors rather than predators, and that the many honorable police become the forces for change.

I wish guns were used only in hunting for food, not on human victims.

I wish that health care workers will stay healthy and willing to remain in their vital roles as they courageously and selflessly fight this opportunistic virus for all of us.

I wish that doctors and nurses did not have to be stand-ins for families who cannot be present to say goodbye to their dying loved ones.

I wish that our national health care advisors would speak out firmly with their unique expertise and firm guidance driven by science.

I wish that our grandchildren, who are our future, could safely return to school and that their teachers will be appreciated for the expertise they have to educate them--but not until it is safe for them all to do so.

I wish that all of our citizens had the benefit of internet access for information, or medical care, and that they and their children could have access to remote learning until they can safely resume class attendance.

I wish that black lives matter, that brown lives matter, that yellow lives matter, that LGBTQ lives matter as much as white lives matter.

I wish that voting will be safe, inclusive, and without subversion so that John R. Lewis may rest in peace after his long, noble, and exhaustive efforts toward that end.

I wish our November election will show that people have paid attention to the lessons of the past, and the fragility of our democracy.

As for myself--

I wish I could invite friends and family to a jubilant post-pandemic party.

And mostly, I wish I could hug my four grandchildren someday soon.

Caroline Kalfas

SPACE TO GROW

My mission on the last day of May is to clean up the front-yard flowerbed. The rocky dirt lays bare, devoid of mulch. A once-vibrant tree with purple leaves now pruned of dead branches looks like something from the pages of a Dr. Seuss book. Unidentified greenery needs trimming and shaping. The only plants I know by name are the chrysanthemums rescued from my neighbor's trash pile and stuck in the ground last fall. The rest of the green sprigs are weeds.

For more than two months, the state of New Jersey has been under stay-at-home orders due to the Covid-19 pandemic. While most people have scaled back and moved the bulk of their interactions online, the Earth has moved forward with spring and produced an abundance of flowers, grass, and weeds that need taming. Going outside for exercise, to check on the weather, or even to do unwanted yard work feels like a welcome opportunity.

Putting on two layers of gloves because I don't like to get my hands dirty, I grab a trash can, clippers, and a hoe and start to sweat.

Across the street, an army of landscapers shows up to do three of my neighbors' yards.

Show-offs! Armed with noisy riding mowers, fancy edgers, and power blowers, they attack the lawns with vicious blades, trimmer lines, and mechanical wind spurts while I sit on my green footstool pulling up unwanted vegetation--roots and all--by hand. I've hardly made a dent in the overgrowth before the landscape army conquers, retreats, and heads to the next block.

Red-faced and itchy, my instinct is to give up. I have other options. A cup of coffee would be nice. Reading a book in the backyard hammock under a shade tree sounds good. I could raid my piggy bank and hire the landscape army to finish the job.

My teenaged son emerges from the house to check on my progress. He presents me with a noble opportunity to abandon my work.

"I've been waiting for the astronauts to arrive at the space station," he says, taking a seat on the front cement steps and staring at his phone. "They've docked. I'm just waiting for them to come out. It's taking forever. Do you want to see?"

I am vaguely familiar with the previous day's launch of American astronauts Robert Behnken and Douglas Hurley on board SpaceX's Crew Dragon. Their trip from Kennedy Space Center in Florida marks the first time that astronauts have gone into space from American soil in almost ten years.

On the screen I see what looks like the area at the end of a boarding bridge where passengers enter an airplane for their flight, except the doors are closed. An American flag and a candy-cane striped exit sign hang above the entryway.

Soon two men who have left the planet's chaos to live and work on board the International Space Station come into view.

Behnken dressed in khaki pants and a deep-blue polo shirt swims through the air, arms stretched forward like he's starting the breast stroke. He emerges all smiles from a white tunnel and embraces one of three men dressed in light blue coveralls, giving him a strong hug. He moves aside and greets the two other fellow astronauts while Hurley makes a similar arrival, appearing to slightly bump his head coming through the door.

"They are like little birds hatching from eggs," I say.

I'm overtaken with emotion. These two men who represent the United States agreed to catapult themselves into the stars to do research and maintain a moving space station. Yet their bravery goes mostly unnoticed in a country immersed in fear and power struggles a short distance of about 220 miles below their spacecraft orbit.

For a mesmerized moment, the explorers captivate me. I don't think about ventilators, masks, washing my hands or social distancing; or the closings of parks, schools, businesses, restaurants, gyms, beaches, churches, medical and dental offices; or systemic racism, protest marches, tear gas, toppled statues, arson, riots, or vandalism. I silence nagging worries about invasions of the spotted lantern fly, sea pollution, melting glaciers, killer bee swarms, earthquakes and hurricanes; and fake news, social media, elections, flattening the curve, infection ratios, unemployment, curfews, and quarantines.

Our nation's problems overwhelm me, but the astronauts didn't float into the sky on a whim or on their own. They demonstrate what can happen when dedicated scientists, astronomers, and engineers collaborate. They show that Americans working collectively toward a common goal can achieve what appears impossible.

They give me hope.

For now, my job is to stay home and try to remain healthy. Like the astronauts, I turn my attention to tasks that can be done in my isolated space. Stretching my back with a rebirth of energy, I stand up and grasp the hoe. My son grabs a shovel from the garage. Together we beautify our landscape until the results complement the yards across the street.

"Tomorrow, let's tackle the rose garden," I say, pleased with today's results but frustrated that we missed a few spots. Yardwork never ends.

After a short discussion, we decide to start the new project now. I drink a cup of coffee to re-fuel and then drift back outside through the garage door.

When the astronauts look out their windows in space, I imagine they see my manicured yard as a part of their glorious view. And no matter how advanced and accommodating the International Space Station becomes, I hope that Earth–despite its problems – remains more desirable than Mars, and the astronauts want to come back home.

Pat Valdata

ELEGY FOR TOILET PAPER

You spanned the shelves
in plastic bundles: one-
ply, two-ply, bonus extra
jumbo rolls. Sometimes you
were recycled, a tad scratchy,
other times you were so soft
you were almost useless. Yet
- - - - - - - - - - - - - - - - - - -
we counted you a necessity,
light-years better than leaves,
corncobs (how did that work,
anyway?), pages torn from
the old Montgomery Ward
catalog. In the outhouse, your
tube a cozy spot for spiders.
- - - - - - - - - - - - - - - - - - -
You came in handy when we
ran out of Kleenex, or when
we needed to wipe splotched
eyeliner or a blob of Clearasil.
When the curse came early,
thick folds of you bought us
time to run to the drugstore.

- - - - - - - - - - - - - - - - - - - -

Nowadays, dear absent friend,
forward thinkers, thinking aft,
who installed upscale bidets
sit smug and clean. The rest
of us count every precious
square to see just how much
we can get away with.

Jack Mackey

PANDEMIC BLUES DAY 43:
IN WHICH I INVITE THE GERMS IN

I busy myself making
sourdough starter,
involving ingredients I don't have
to shop for–flour and water, and hope
a few sympathetic microbes will fly
into my kitchen alive and ready to work,
leaven this flat feeling that our lockdown
could last what's left of my life. I'm doing whatever
keeps me from sleeping
all day, drinking too much.
On YouTube the helpful man uses just
a measuring cup, eschews
a digital scale and all its romantic precision.
Just eyeball it, leave something to chance, he says.
This recipe for anarchy, his casual approach
suits me fine. I think of all the things
you can do just enough–

like a life–chug along for years without a plan,
dump Tinkertoys onto the carpet
knowing a few pieces are lost,
make what you can
or take a road trip in an old car
with squiggly line signs to warn you
of the cliff, but not when you'll meet it.

A carefree journey marked
by ambiguous symbology, open to interpretation
open to hope–

So when the gloppy mess goes rancid after a few days
I pour it down the drain, mix a new batch of chaos,
lid the jar loosely, open a window, and
welcome in the air from outside.

Kay Drew

A PANDEMIC OFFERING

I am offering my breath to you.* Molecules of oxygen and nitrogen and carbon dioxide from my lungs to yours, just as those same molecules once entered and exited the lungs of other people on the far side of the world. If your own breath is insufficient right now, perhaps this will help.

Air connects us, just as the need to breathe does, even in this time when breathing close to each other is prohibited, when masks hinder the movement of molecules. Masks or no, your breath and mine will slowly, slowly make their way across the planet, to be taken in by so many others: the man in Wuhan who has lost his mother to the virus; the doctor in Italy who can finally afford to be exhausted, now that the worst of the siege is over; the woman in New York City recovering from coronavirus's onslaught and haunted by her memories of the ICU—the swishing and knocking of the ventilator, the nurse in his space-suit gently changing her compression socks, the medical team talking about her in low voices just outside her door. My breath and yours, drawn in by a homeless person huddled over a tattered plastic bag of possessions, dying of the virus alone in an alley at night; by a child in a torn dress, crying for her sick parents in a favela where there is no water for handwashing, no social distancing.

Someday we will be allowed to mingle our breath once more—in laughter and joy at being able to hug and kiss again, in tears and wailing for those we have lost. We will not have to wear masks and stay six feet apart to celebrate smaller weddings than we had planned. We will no longer have to visit with our assisted-living grandparents through their windows or arrange drive-by birthday parties for our children. Graduations will once again be joyful rites of passage with diplomas passed from living hand to living hand instead of virtual shadows of the real thing. We will finally have those memorial services for the loved ones who had the misfortune of dying during the pandemic, whether of COVID-19 or not.

Remember, when that time of quarantine constraint is over, that our breathing and our sharing of this precious air has always been and will always be a treasure. A reminder that we are all one.

inspired by "I Am Offering This Poem" by Jimmy Santiago Baca

Stephanie King LaMotte

"I'D LIKE TO TEACH THE WORLD TO SING....."

Before, my weeks were filled with music. Rehearsals with choirs and ensembles, big and small, made squeezing in dinner challenging. From an elite 14-voice a cappella group, to a large community chorus, many nights of the week were devoted to rehearsal time. Sunday was a work day with choir practice and church services. The rest of the week was filled with choosing music from hundreds of options, planning musical programs, making rehearsal tracks, composing new music, or practicing the piano. Ah yes... the joys and stresses of a choir director's life! I love it and miss it desperately.

The coronavirus thief broke in and stole my livelihood, as he did for so many others. It was crazy the way everything ground to a halt. Not knowing much about the virus back in March, we still realized right away that getting together was a bad idea. During one weekend, all the performing arts groups in town decided to suspend rehearsals and performances for a few weeks. We were shocked, but knew it would only be for a short while. So, I happily hunkered down at home and attacked projects that had been on the back burner—organizing files, going through the storage unit, putting photo albums together. It was great to have time to be quiet at home and get things done. For a while. Until it wasn't.

As the leader of numerous groups, I had a responsibility to learn all I could about this deadly virus. I watched the news, read the papers, and scoured the internet for breaking stories. I missed my singers, and wanted to know how soon we could safely be back together.

Meanwhile, beginning with the second week at home, I started writing a weekly newsletter to my choirs, as a way to stay connected and encourage them as best I could. Sometimes I sent music to sing, or links to listen to. I sent stories about how songs were written, and articles about the composers who wrote them. Soon I was sending photos, and writing more personal stories about my life with my husband at home on the Chesapeake Bay. I put together questionnaires to find out more about the choir members, and turned them in to quiz games for all to enjoy. "I rode in a hot air balloon in New Mexico. Who am I?"

As a country, we were pulling together to fight this virus, until we weren't. Small cracks became crevices, then death-defying canyons, and soon we couldn't hear each other because everyone was shouting at once. Republicans and Democrats both defiant and sure their side is right. At least, black and white came together to insist on racial equality and a re-evaluation of the hate that divides us.

We wrestled with the great injustices being repeated year after year, and decade after decade, and longed to do more, do *something*, anything to let our dear brothers and sisters know we are one with them. Time ticks on as we question right and wrong, and discover greater and greater injustices as a regular occurrence and *pattern*, far more than we even realized. We long for change and are determined that this time will be different, that the thousands and millions of voices united together MUST be heard. We hope, and we pray, and we breathe.

As passions ran deep, I incorporated these current events in to my newsletters, and the "Tuesday Tidings" became something the choir members looked forward to. I wanted to stay connected—to keep spirits high, to remind us that we are a team and are there for each other. It was great, but it wasn't the same. Where is the music?

Music enriches our lives like nothing else. You know that favorite song that brings a smile to your face the instant it starts to play? A song conjures up a place—the smell, the taste, the memory of being there. Music engages our emotions, and stirs up our passions. We feel, we sense, we sigh, we smile.

As choirs and singers around the world were stuck at home, the internet was flooded with special renditions of favorite songs. Everyone rushed to create a "Zoom-like" recording that featured voices and photos woven throughout a tapestry of song. I was bombarded by choir members asking if WE could do that, assuming it was simply a matter of planning a Zoom meeting and singing together. But no! It doesn't work that way. Because of latency issues and lagging internet speeds, we cannot all sing together in a virtual meeting. We tried it, and it was hysterically funny, because it didn't work AT ALL! You would perhaps hear a voice here or there, but nobody was singing together. It was funny, and it was sad, all at the same time.

Of course, it *is* possible to produce a beautiful recording with proper equipment, recording individual voices and instruments from home, then having a trained producer put it all together. It sounds lovely, but is not the experience of singing in an ensemble. People join choirs because they like to sing, *yes*, but it is much deeper than that. It is the joy of making new friends, sharing in a common hobby, working together to accomplish a lofty goal. Singing in a choir is fabulous, and we all miss it dearly.

If you had told me back in the beginning of March that *singing* would be one of the most dangerous things you could do, I would have laughed out loud! Are you kidding me?! But that's exactly what is happening with Covid-19's assiduous move among us. Worse than sneezing or coughing, singing can propel the virus much farther due to the way a singer breathes deeply and engages the entire body in producing a pleasing sound. Instead of a 6-foot social distancing standard, singers must stand 16 feet apart to be safe.

It is a sobering truth that singing is just too dangerous right now. In early summer, most choir programs cancelled all upcoming Fall rehearsals and programming. We are hoping against hope that we can sing in the Spring, either through the creation of a vaccine, or perhaps new ways of screening for the virus or preventing its spread that we are unaware of right now. Reality strikes fear in our hearts, but hope springs eternal.

My husband is not a musician, but loves to listen to music and sing along. He played an Andrea Bocelli song for me the other day, and out of the blue, I started crying. Music is the beauty of life. Music reaches deep inside and tugs on our heart strings. It is the color in the rainbow, and the understanding of our humanity. Music is passion and music is love. No wonder we miss it so!

"I'd like to teach the world to sing...in perfect harmony!" We may not be able to sing or harmonize in a choir the way we want to right now, but together, we hold on to HOPE, knowing that day will come. As a people, we can choose to put aside differences, sow harmony and peace, and find a healthy way of living. Music is within and around us, and will empower us to overcome the bully coronavirus. Without music there is no life, and without life there is no music. Keep breathing, keep singing, keep loving. Sing and thrive. Live on.

CONTRIBUTORS

PAMELA ANDREWS from Salisbury, Maryland, is retired from a 25 year career as program director of Delmarva Public Radio, where she also produced annual music festivals featuring regional classical music performers. Ms. Andrews, currently president of the Lyme Disease Association of Delmarva, advocates for patients, and has produced medical conferences to educate on tick-borne diseases. *The Lyme Wars* is her first novel, describing the adversities faced by patients with chronic Lyme disease.

CHRISTINE BRENNAN moved to the Eastern Shore of Maryland from New York five years ago. Formerly a journalist and a corporate communications executive, she is new to writing fiction; "Suburban Affairs" is her third published short story. In addition to writing for her own amusement, she is currently a Registered Nurse at the University of Maryland Shore Medical Center at Easton. She also writes the Health Corner column for the American Brittany Rescue Association. Christine lives on Tilghman Island with her husband, their French Brittany and several laying hens.

JAMIE BROWN, author of *The Delaware Bay: Poems* (named Best Chapbook of Poetry 2020 by the Delaware Press Association), of *Sakura* (named Best Book of Verse 2014 by D.P.A.), *Conventional Heresies*, a full-length collection of poetry from Bay Oak Publishers, and *Freeholder*, from Argonne House Press, founded *The Broadkill Review*, and publishes books from The Broadkill River Press and chapbooks from The Broadkill Press. He is a poet, author (fiction-and-nonfiction), an award-winning playwright, scholar, and teacher (George Washington University, Georgetown University, the Smithsonian Institution, University of Delaware, Wesley College), and former Poetry Critic for *The Washington Times*. In September 2016 he suffered from an aortic dissection, from which he is one of a very small percentage to survive.

PATRICIA BUDD is a retired computer engineer (math is her alternate language) who lives in Portland, the "right" coast, of Maine with her husband Richard, a theoretical physicist/bridge player. They have two sons, three grandchildren, and a great-grandson. She is a Reiki Master, nutrition coach, and gardener - and has published in *The Maine Review*, *Anderbo*, *Night & Sparrow*, and *The MacGuffin* among other journals and Web sites.

CATHERINE CARTER's collections of poetry include *Larvae of the Nearest Stars*, *The Swamp Monster at Home*, *The Memory of Gills*, all with LSU Press, and *Marks of the Witch* (Jacar Press, 2014.) Her work has also appeared in *Best American Poetry 2009*, *Orion*, *Poetry*, and *Ploughshares*, among others.

CAROL CASEY lives in in Betterton, a small waterfront town located where the Chesapeake Bay and Sassafras River meet. Her poetry has been published in *CRUX*, the literary magazine of The Catholic University of America; in the *National Catholic Reporter*; in the *Kent County News*; and in *Bay to Ocean 2019*. Her poem "How to Make a Beach" from *Bay to Ocean 2019* was nominated for a Pushcart Prize.

Writer and poet, JOAN DRESCHER COOPER finds inspiration in nature, her family, and her students. Her debut poetry collection, *Birds Like Me,* was published by Finishing Line Press in 2019. Her poetry, book reviews, and fiction have appeared in *The Delmarva Review 2020*, *River Babble*, *Doorknobs & Body Paint* and the *Sand Dune Anthology 2019*. Joan has self-published two novels and a collection of short stories through Salt Water Media: *Finding Home on Lilac Hill, Return to Lilac Hill,* and *Lilac Hill Folly.* Website: www.joandcooper.com and Twitter: @WordGin @BirdsLikeMe1

KRISTIN W. DAVIS is a former journalist based in Washington, DC, and a poetry student in the Stonecoast MFA program at the University of Southern Maine. She enjoys choral singing, word games and leading contemplative meditation. Her journalism has appeared in *Kiplinger's* Magazine, *Reader's Digest*, *Redbook*, *U.S. News and World Report* and the *Washington Post*, and her poetry in *Passager*, *THINK*, and *What Rough Beast*.

TINA RAYE DAYTON grew up on the Eastern Shore of Maryland and received her MFA in Writing from Sarah Lawrence College. She is the 2012 Dogfish Head Poetry Prize winner and author of the chapbook, *The Softened Ground*. Tina's poems have appeared in *The Delmarva Review, Potomac Review, The Broadkill Review*, and a number of other journals. Pre-pandemic, Tina worked as a preschool teacher. These days she's homeschooling her 9-year old, accepting freelance editing projects, and baking loads of banana bread.

MEG EDEN's work is published or forthcoming in magazines including *Prairie Schooner, Poetry Northwest, Crab Orchard Review, RHINO* and *CV2*. She teaches creative writing at Anne Arundel Community College. She is the author of five poetry chapbooks, the novel *"Post-High School Reality Quest"* (2017), and the poetry collection *"Drowning in the Floating World"* (2020). She runs the Magfest MAGES Library blog, which posts accessible academic articles about video games (https://super.magfest.org/mages-blog). Find her online at www.megedenbooks.com or on Twitter at @ConfusedNarwhal.

TARA A. ELLIOTT's poems have appeared in *TAOS Journal of International Poetry & Art, The American Journal of Poetry*, and *Stirring,* among others. A fellow of the Virginia Center for the Creative Arts (VCCA) and a past Poet-in-Residence of Freeman State, she currently serves as the President Elect of the non-profit, Eastern Shore Writers Association, the director of Maryland's Salisbury Poetry Week, and the co-chair of the Bay to Ocean Writers Conference. She is honored to have been awarded two Light of Literacy Awards and the MD Humanities Christine D. Sarbanes Award for her work in education and community outreach.

KRIS FAATZ's short fiction has appeared or is forthcoming in various journals including *The Baltimore Review, Kenyon Review Online*, and *100 Word Story*, and has received recognition in several competitions, most recently winning *Tiferet Journal's* 2020 fiction contest. Her first novel, *To Love A Stranger* (Blue Moon Publishers, 2017), was a finalist for the 2016 Schaffner Press Music in Literature Award. She has been a teaching fellow at the Kenyon Review Writers Workshops and a contributor at the Sewanee Writers' Conference, and is a resident of Baltimore, where she teaches creative writing with the public library system, Community College of Baltimore County, and Baltimore Bridges. She is also a performing pianist.

JUNE FORTE's short stories, personal essays, articles and photographs have been featured in literary, magazines, newspapers, and anthologies. Her nonfiction articles and photographs have appeared in daily, weekly, and monthly newspapers and magazines. Past president of the Virginia Writers Club, she also served on the Poetry Society of Virginia's Advisory Board. She established the Poet Laureate position in Prince William County, Virginia in 2014. June enjoys the challenge of style and format hopping.

COURTNEY FOSTER is the mother of two daughters and the daughter of two parents from Prince George's County Maryland. As a fulltime lawyer, part time writer, and all the time daydreamer, she is thrilled to have her first short story published in *ESWA's 2020 Anthology*. Stay tuned for more.

CHRISTOPHER T. GEORGE was born in Liverpool, England, in 1948. He emigrated to the US in 1955, but returned home to experience the "Swinging Sixties." He re-emigrated to the US in 1968 and studied poetry with Sister Maura Eichner and Elliott Coleman. He has been published in such journals as *Poet Lore, Smoke, Bogg, Electric Acorn, Anti-Heroin Chic,* and *Triplopia*. A former editor at *Loch Raven Review*, Chris has a poetry site at http://chrisgeorge.netpublish.net/. He lives with his wife Donna in Newark, Delaware. As a published historian of the War of 1812 in the Chesapeake, Chris is a consultant on the film script "Storm and Garrison" written with West Virginia writer ABEL NOBEL.

Dedicated to empowering our country's future leaders and marginalized groups, AMBER GREEN has served as a Youth Development Specialist for her local city government, sits on both the Youth Development Advisory Committee and Human Rights Advisory Committee, and founded Fenix Youth Project Inc., a creative arts youth development 501(c)3 non-profit organization focused on empowering youth to create social change while using art as a tool.

DAVID J. HOFFMAN is a Scientist Emeritus ecotoxicologist with the US Geological Survey, and a former adjunct Professor with Frostburg University and UMD. He lives in Bivalve, MD and also spends time in Old Lyme, CT as a trustee for the Florence Griswold Museum of art. He is the author of over 175 scientific publications including books, book chapters, and reviews. He has served on multiple editorial boards. *Handbook of Ecotoxicology* was a best seller for CRC Press. He is working on a series of short fiction, with his second short story in ESWA Bay to Ocean Anthology.

MICHAEL D. JONES transitioned from Michigan to (Towson) Maryland last year. This spring Finishing Line Press published his poetry chapbook, *Return of the Orb Weaver*. He has two collections of poetry (*Unlikely Trees* (2014) and *Overtime and The Dance* (2017)), two Pushcart Prize nominated poems, one award winning poem, frequently teaches poetry segments at local schools when not engaged in nonprofit development work, and enjoys hiking and mild winters. http://www.michaeljonesmipoet.com/ http://www.facebook.com/jonesmipoet

CAROLINE KALFAS is a former newspaper journalist who lives in Woolwich Township, New Jersey. Her poetry has been recognized by the Pennsylvania Poetry Society, and her haiku appears in the Haiku Society of America's spring/summer 2020 edition of *Frogpond*. Her essays also are included in the 2018 and 2019 editions of *Bay to Ocean*. To read more of her work visit carolinechatter.wordpress.com.

KAREN KENDRA is a retired RN and Certified Legal Nurse Consultant. She moved to Chester, Maryland in 2013. With Peer Learning Partnership, she co-facilitated a writing course and guide for fellow retirees.

ELLEN KRAWCZAK is retired and enjoying the quiet life on Maryland's Eastern Shore. Her work background is varied – she was a paralegal in a New York City Law firm, and a real estate settlement officer and a substitute teacher in Maryland.

MICHELLE KREINER lives with her husband, daughter, and a menagerie of pets in Catonsville, Md. She loves spending summers in Ocean City and Berlin, Md. One of her favorite things to do is write outside peering at a beautiful view. Michelle finds the Atlantic Ocean to be her strongest muse.

She has an associates in early childhood education and a bachelors in English. Previous publication credits include *The Muse* and *Life As An [insert label here]*.

DOUG LAMBDIN is a high school teacher in Baltimore, Maryland. He has published prose and poetry in several journals and magazines, including *The Baltimore Review, Urbanite Magazine, BootsnAll, Education Week Teacher Magazine, The Baltimore Sun*, and in the anthology *Listening to the Birth of Crystals*. This spring he attended the Bay to Ocean Writer's Conference for the first time, and he is very much looking forward to going again next year.

STEPHANIE KING LAMOTTE moved to Chestertown, Maryland in 2017. Ms. LaMotte is the Music Director and Choirmaster at Emmanuel Church, the Assistant Director and Accompanist of the Chester River Chorale, and the Director of River Voices. Stephanie lives on the Chesapeake Bay with her husband, fellow writer Richard LaMotte. As a writer and musician, she focuses on songwriting, poetry, non-fiction articles, and short stories for adults and children. Stephanie may be contacted at sksimplify@gmail.com

NATALIE LOBE's full length book of poetry, *What Gypsies Don't Know*, was published in October 2018. Chapbooks, *Conversation with Abraham*, was published in 2012, *Island Time* in 2008 and *Connected Voices* in 2006. Her poems have appeared in *Slant, Jewish Currents, Comstock Review*, and many others. She has taught poetry as a Poet in the Schools, teaches at Anne Arundel Community College and to other adult groups. Natalie has also taught short story and memoir writing. She reviewed poetry for Montserrat Review for two years and has been poetry and writing judge for, "Poetry Out Loud" and St. John's College's senior arts contest. Natalie is a graduate of Connecticut College and the University of New Hampshire.

JACK MACKEY lives in Southern Delaware. He holds a master's degree in English from the University of Maryland. His poetry has been anthologized by Darkhouse Books and the Rehoboth Beach Writers' Guild. Poems have appeared in *Mojave River Review, Rat's Ass Review, Mobius, Writer's Resist, Third Wednesday, Anti-Heroin Chic, The Broadkill Review*, and others.

NANCY McCLOY is a retired special education teacher and administrator who lives with her husband in the village of Still Pond on Maryland's Eastern Shore. Inspiration for her poems often comes while watching the sun rise, observing nature, taking long walks, and from the ordinary events of everyday life. She has had poems included in the Art of Stewardship exhibits at River Arts in Chestertown, one an honorable mention, as well as in the 2018, 2019, and upcoming 2020 Bay to Ocean anthologies. She was a finalist for the Crossroads Competition sponsored by ESWA.

SARAH McGREGOR is a former speech/language pathologist, lifelong equestrian, and author of the romance novels *Indecent Proposal* and *He Loves Me Knot*. She lives on a farm near Fair Hill Maryland with her husband and an assortment of animals. Check out her website at sarahmcgregorauthor. com and follow her on instagram at sbs.mcgregor and Facebook.

NANCY MITCHELL is a 2012 Pushcart Prize winner and the author of *The Near Surround, Grief Hut* and *The Out-of-Body Shop*, and co-editor of *Plume Interviews I*. Her poems have appeared in journal such as *Agni, Green Mountains Review, Washington Square Review* and *Superstition Review*. She serves as Associate Editor of Special Features and Interviews for Plume Poetry, and is the inaugural Poet Laureate of the City of Salisbury Maryland

GEORGE R. MERRILL, an Episcopal priest and essayist, is co-author of *Reflections: Psychological and Spiritual Images of the Heart*, and the author of *The Bay of the Mother of God: A Yankee Discovers the Chesapeake Bay*. His essays have appeared in regional and national magazines, the literary journal, *The Delmarva Review* and they air on Delmarva Public Radio. George's essays appear weekly in *The Talbot Spy*, a regional online newspaper.

JANE EDNA MOHLER is the author of *Broken Umbrellas* (Kelsay, 2019.) She is the current Bucks County Poet Laureate. She is 2016 winner of Main Street Voices, a Pushcart Prize nominee, and a Robert Fraser finalist. Her poems have, or will soon appear, in *Gargoyle, Schuylkill Valley Journal, U.S.1 Worksheets, River Heron Review, The Skinny Poetry Journal, Bay to Ocean Anthology*, and the *Boston Globe*. She was a presenter at the 2020 BTO Writer's conference.

MARY PAUER has received three literary fellowhips from the Delaware Division of Arts in fiction and creative nonfiction. Her work can be read in *Southern Women's Review, The Fox Chase Review, Delmarva Review, Delaware Today, The Chaos,* and *The Avocet,* among others, and in anthologies featuring locan authors. Her work has national recognition, including the Sally Reinhart Award and several National Press Association awards. Her new collection, *Traveling Moons,* won the 2018 Delaware Press award for book poetry. Portions of sales from the book are donated to horse rescue at the SPCA in Kent County Delaware.

NINA PHILLIPS is a writer and teacher. She self-published two plays about Bulgaria's rescue of their Jews in the Holocaust. *The Crushing of the Roses* is in the Holocaust section in the Brandywine Library in Wilmington, Delaware and was acknowledged by Eric Rubin, the former U.S. Ambassador to Bulgaria. After living in New Mexico for 20 years, she returned to her native Delaware in 1995 and lives in Wilmington.

KATIE AIKEN RITTER's work has been featured in local newspapers and local and national magazines. She served as launch editor and primary writer for a hyper-regional magazine. Katie has published three novels set in Iceland in the Viking era: *The Plains of Althing, Thunder Horse,* and *The Green Land,* and she plans two more sequels for her Norse Adventure series. Katie is an Alabama Writers Conference Novel Award winner, and a Pirate's Alley Faulkner Society finalist. Although she lives near Baltimore, her heart belongs to the tidewater rivers and fields of the Eastern Shore. You may reach Katie via:

Website . . . . .www.katieaikenritter.com
Instagram . . . . . .@KatieRitterVikingWriter
Facebook. . . . . . .@KatieRitterVikingWriter
Goodreads . . . . .Katie Aiken Ritter
Amazon . . . . . . .Katie Aiken Ritter

KIM ROBERTS is the editor of *By Broad Potomac's Shore: Great Poems from the Early Days of our Nation's Capital* (University of Virginia Press, 2020), and the author of *A Literary Guide to Washington, DC: Walking in the Footsteps of American Writers from Francis Scott Key to Zora Neale Hurston* (University of

Virginia Press, 2018), and five books of poems, most recently *The Scientific Method* (WordTech Editions, 2017). http://www.kimroberts.org

DONNA ROTHERT is a retired corporate executive and former high school teacher dividing her time between Delmarva and Reston VA. A native Marylander, who has lived and worked in Texas, Connecticut, and Virginia, she has traveled to forty-eight of the fifty states. Her essays appeared in the 30th Anniversary Anthology of the Maryland Writers' Association, *Thirty Ways to Love Maryland*, and a short story received a Judge's Award in the 2019 *Beach Dreams*.

CHERYL SADOWSKI writes personal and lyric essays from her home in Northern Virginia, where she also works in nonprofit branding and marketing. Cheryl's writing explores memory, art, culture and the natural world. She recently received honorable mention in ESWA's 2020 Crossroads Contest. Follow Cheryl on Instagram @cherylsadowski.

CATHERINE R. SEELEY, M.A., is retired from a career in health care administration; medical ethics; crisis, loss, grief and transition. She has been a consultant/educator for hospices, long-term care facilities, hospitals, and health care systems around the country. Catherine's poem, "Eire," was selected for inclusion in the Eastern Shore Writers Association anthology in 2019. Her book of poetry, *Beauty Noticed*, will be released in Autumn, 2020.

SHARON K. SHEPPARD is a transplant from Minnesota to Magnolia, Delaware. Writing poetry has kept her curious, and in a state of wonder for nearly 40 years. She loves to look closely, find connections, and illuminate that which is not immediately obvious. Sharon has self-published six books of poetry, her most recent being *The Brilliance of the Stain* (2019).

LAURA SHOVAN is an editor, educator, poet, and children's author based in Clarksville, Maryland. Her books include *Mountain, Log, Salt and Stone*, winner of the Harriss Poetry Prize, *Life in Me Like Grass on Fire: Love Poems*, and several award-winning novels for children. Her work appears in many literary journals and children's poetry anthologies. Laura co-hosts Wilde Readings in Howard

County. She is a longtime Maryland State Arts Council poet-in-the-schools. Website: www.laurashovan.com. Social media: @laurashovan.

SEAN SUN graduated from the University of Kentucky with MS in Statistics in 1993 and the University of Maryland Eastern Shore with MS in Applied Computer Science in 1997. He lives in Salisbury and works as a programmer at the University of Maryland Eastern Shore. He is from China and English is his second language. He often writes poems in his native tongue and very recently has started dabbling in writing poems in English-- a significant challenge even though he has been in the states for more than 32 years. He is good at Chinese Calligraphy and singing, and loves gardening. His motto is: Life is a struggle, so face it!

PAT VALDATA's poetry book about women aviation pioneers, *Where No Man Can Touch*, won the 2015 Donald Justice Poetry Prize. Her other poetry titles are *Inherent Vice* and *Looking for Bivalve*. Her poetry has been published in *Ecotone*, *Fledgling Rag*, *Italian Americana*, *Little Patuxent Review*, and *Valparaiso Poetry Review*. She has a new novel, *Eve's Daughters*, forthcoming from Moonshine Cove Publishing in November. Pat is a retired adjunct professor who lives in Crisfield, Maryland, with her husband Bob Schreiber. www.patvaldata.com

CHARLOTTE ZANG resides near the Chester River in Chestertown, Maryland. Her work has appeared in *Mused Literary Review* (Spring 2012 and Fall 2012). She published a chapbook titled *Night Travels* in 2015. She is a business marketing and content copywriter as well as a coach for first-time authors.

RICHARD ZAPPA is a trial lawyer and novelist. He is the author of the crime drama thriller, Identical Misfortune (AIA Publishing, 2020). A Delaware Super Lawyer, he has litigated and tried numerous cases in federal and state court, many resulting in multimillion dollar recoveries for his clients. He retired in 2018 to write novels full time. A black belt martial artist and self-taught pianist, he writes from his homes in Wilmington and Rehoboth Beach, Delaware and St. Thomas, Virgin Islands.

2020 EDITORIAL BOARD

TARA A. ELLIOTT's poems have appeared in *TAOS Journal of International Poetry & Art*, *The American Journal of Poetry*, and *Stirring*, among others. A fellow of the Virginia Center for the Creative Arts (VCCA) and a past Poet-in-Residence of Freeman State, she currently serves as the President Elect of the non-profit, Eastern Shore Writers Association, the director of Maryland's Salisbury Poetry Week, and the co-chair of the Bay to Ocean Writers Conference. She is honored to have been awarded two Light of Literacy Awards and the MD Humanities Christine D. Sarbanes Award for her work in education and community outreach.

ELLEN KRAWCZAK is retired and enjoying the quiet life on Maryland's Eastern Shore. Her work background is varied – she was a paralegal in a New York City Law firm, and a real estate settlement officer and a substitute teacher in Maryland.

RUSSELL REECE's poems, stories and essays have appeared or are forthcoming in a variety of journals and anthologies such as *Gargoyle*, *Blueline*, *Under the Gum Tree*, *The 3288 Review* and *Proud to Be: Writing by American Warriors*. Russ has received fellowships from the Delaware Division of the Arts and the Virginia Center for the Creative Arts. In 2019 he won the Pat Herold Nielsen Poetry Prize in Chester River Art's Art of Stewardship contest. His writing has received Pushcart and Best of the Net nominations as well as awards from the Delaware Press Association, the Faulkner-Wisdom competition and others.

EMILY RICH is a writer, editor, and teacher. Her work has been featured in *Little Patuxent Review*, *Delmarva Review*, *the Pinch*, *Hippocampus*, *CutBank*, and others. She has twice been featured as a notable in the annual *Best American Essays* collection.

DONNA ROTHERT is a retired corporate executive and former high school teacher dividing her time between Delmarva and Reston VA. A native Marylander, who has lived and worked in Texas, Connecticut, and Virginia, she has traveled to forty-eight of the fifty states. Her essays appeared in the 30th Anniversary Anthology of the Maryland Writers' Association, *Thirty Ways to Love Maryland*, and a short story received a Judge's Award in the 2019 *Beach Dreams*.

COVER ARTIST

LAURA AMBLER is an international award winning author, published illustrator, produced playwright, and multiply optioned and produced screenwriter. She is a member of the Writers Guild of America and the Dramatists Guild. Ambler resides in Easton, MD and has been a member of the Eastern Shore Writers Association, Design Editor of *Delmarva Review*, volunteer for the Bay to Ocean Writers Conference, and the 2012 Rehoboth Beach Film Festival Artist. She dedicates this cover art to the memory of longtime friend and creative collaborator, Mala Burt

Made in the USA
Middletown, DE
06 April 2021